CATS OF THE WORLD

World Wildlife Series I. General Editor: Bruce Campbell

CATS
OF THE WORLD

Armand Denis

ILLUSTRATED WITH PHOTOGRAPHS

HOUGHTON MIFFLIN COMPANY BOSTON

The Riverside Press Cambridge

1 9 6 4

Also by Armand Denis: On Safari

Acknowledgments

THE FACTS about the natural history of the cat family contained in this book could not have been assembled without a great deal of help from many friends and authorities. I should particularly like to thank R. W. Hayman of the Mammal Section at the British Museum (Natural History); also Sir Alan Herbert for permission to reproduce part of his poem on page 5 and, for general assistance, the Librarian of the Zoological Society of London and his staff, Sergeant Marvin L. Jones, Dr. Paul Leyhausen of the Max Planck Institut at Wuppertal, Mrs. Dorothy Reville of the New York Zoological Society, and Dr. Ernest P. Walker of Washington, D.C. I hope I have acknowledged all individual items of information in the text.

Owing to my distance from libraries and other sources it fell to Bruce Campbell as editor of the series to do a considerable amount of checking for me at all stages of the book's progress, and I am very grateful to him for this assistance.

The photographers are given in the list of illustrations. I am deeply indebted for pictures of Asian cats to Frederick W. Champion, who holds the record for species actually photographed in the wild, and to E. P. Gee, now the leading resident authority on Indian wildlife. Nearly all the African photographs are the work of my colleague Des Bartlett and his team, and I am always glad to pay a tribute to their keenness and skill.

Maurice Wilson had the task of "reconstructing" the six species of which we could find no living pictures. Ardent photographer as I am, it is a pleasure for me to show such examples of the most difficult branch of natural history art.

Finally, hoping that many readers will want to help practically in the work of conservation, I give the addresses of organizations operating internationally.

International Union for the Conservation of Nature and Natural Resources (I.U.C.N.), Morges, Lausanne, Switzerland.

Survival Service of I.U.C.N., Morges, Lausanne, Switzerland.

World Wildlife Fund. International office in Morges, Lausanne, Switzerland.

American office: 1816 Jefferson Place N.W., Washington, D.C.

ARMAND DENIS

Nairobi
January 1964

Foreword

IF WE ARE to understand the great problems involved
in conserving nature, it is essential that we should be
well and accurately informed about the many animals
threatened with extinction. I therefore welcome the
publication of this series of books by Constable and
Company, Ltd., and Houghton Mifflin Company in
conjunction with the World Wildlife Fund. Each is
written by a leading authority on his chosen group of
animals, containing rare and interesting species, is
beautifully illustrated, and will be a standard work of
reference as well as a stimulus to the vital task of saving
the world's wildlife and wild places.

H.R.H. PRINCE BERNHARD of the Netherlands
President of the World Wildlife Fund

Preface

THIS BOOK, the first in a series dedicated to the work of the World Wildlife Fund, is an event. Not since 1883 has any book in English attempted to survey the entire cat family — all thirty-five wild species plus the domestic tabby. Books have been written about lions, tigers, jaguars, pumas, and other single species of the feline menage, but it took the courage of Armand Denis to summarize the lot and to bring us up to date on their current status and their chances of survival.

In fact, no one is better qualified to tell us about cats than this able naturalist, living as he does in Nairobi, where *simba* is a neighbor and even leopards sneak in at night to snatch unwary dogs. A world traveler, he knows these graceful animals in the wild, in zoos, and as personal pets. Some of them he has introduced to the British public on the television screen. His show "On Safari" has made his scholarship and engaging manner familiar to millions of Britons; no broadcasts command a greater audience.

In this book the king of beasts, the lion, gets top billing, but our own American lion, the puma — often called the ghost cat — is also treated at length. However, some of us might disagree with the comparative survival rating that Denis applies to these two big carnivores. He rates the lion C, just one category below D (danger); its welfare must be watched with some concern. The puma, on the other hand, is rated A, safe and likely to survive. This may be an astute appraisal, but actually in only eight months of African travel I have seen more than one hundred lions, while during a lifetime of field work in the Americas, from the Canadian wilderness to Patagonia, I have had but one fleeting glimpse of a puma.

Most intriguing are those little-known mystery cats in category Q (for question) — the Chinese desert cat, the sand cat, the pampas cat, the Bornean red cat, the marbled cat, and others.

The comparatively new art of wildlife photography reaches a new peak of excellence in some of the photographs by Des Bartlett and other photographers in this, the first comprehensive collection of cat photographs.

Not merely a catalogue, the book first gives us a dissertation on "What Makes a Cat?" — something of its structure, its biology, its evolution. Cats or catlike animals have been around a long time, in fact the modern genus *Felis* was well developed by the Miocene, ten to twenty-five million years ago, and some extraordinary forms such as the saber-toothed tiger evolved and passed away into the void. The thirty-five wild cat species on earth today are the end products of millions of years of evolution. The World Wildlife Fund (see page 138) is dedicated to the principle that we shall not see them disappear from this earth in our time.

ROGER TORY PETERSON

Contents

Illustrations

1. Cat Appeal

I HAVE BEEN a lover of cats, from the lion to the prize Siamese and the humble alley cat, for as long as I can remember. They have for me an almost irresistible fascination — I must not only watch them, I must touch them, stroke them, and make them respond to me. I have been successful in making friends with many kinds of cat and this has given me a great deal of pleasure. I hope that this book may help me share this pleasure with others, not only with cat lovers but with all who are in any way sensitive to the peculiar appeal of cats.

Wherein lies this appeal? Why do millions of people go to look at the Big Cats in zoos every year? Why did man, able to choose his pets from the broad range of the animal kingdom, pick the relatively unresponsive cat and take it all over the world, to the cities and the farms and the remote islands, thousands of miles from its original Mediterranean home? The explanation, I think, lies in the cat's own basic unresponsiveness — although the word is not well chosen. Cats do respond, but they do so without losing their pride and independence. The fireside pet has no more abdicated it than has the most fierce King of the Jungle. Cats truly belong to two worlds, as Joy Adamson has put it: it is possible to tame a lion or a leopard, to make it accept our will, or rather condescend to our wishes, up to a point; but the gateway to the other world is always wide open. And so it is with the house cat. One moment it is lying apparently fast asleep on the hearthrug; the next it is out in the night, sending its wild music over the jungle of the rooftops, or stalking its prey in the backyard with all the savage concentration of a leopard.

No wonder primitive man everywhere venerated the great cats. From early times he distinguished between their different personalities. The lion might be fierce and ravenous, but it was also noble. The sculptured slabs of Nineveh are probably the oldest remaining portraits of the symbol that many a warrior king or chief delighted to adopt. The Lion of Judah. Richard Coeur de Lion, that evergreen hero of improbable adventures. William the Lion. Many of the later Roman emperors, and many Popes, were called Leo. Venice took as her symbol the Lion of St. Mark. There are innumerable examples. In America the mountain lion also was held in high esteem. Puma was the name the Incas of Peru gave it and it seems to have been royal game; a tribe of Aztecs took their name from it and regarded it as an ancestor; the Cochiti Indians carved two sacred "lions" side by side in the rocks of New Mexico and worshiped there. Is it just chance, or what biologists call convergence, that this smaller American "lion" seems to have held much the same place among these ancient peoples as the larger lion did in Europe? Or is this evidence of a common inheritance far back in time?

The tiger spreads a different aura — great strength certainly, but also ferocity, ruthlessness, a hint of treachery. Few emperors or other rulers called themselves "The Tiger," though their subjects and enemies may have so nicknamed them behind their backs.

The days of chivalry and, we hope, of the tyrant's bloodbath, are over. These fierce names are now used by teams of footballers — with suitably striped jerseys — ice hockey players, and speedway riders, and it is the supporters of the Lions or the Tigers who do the roaring.

But there is no doubt that this different attitude to lions and tigers is founded on observation. There is something indeed majestic and kingly about a lion; his mane helps, of course, but except when roused he has a "mild and magnificent eye" — in fact, the truth is he is a lazy fellow. It is precisely this mixture of indolence and courage that primitive peoples admire. Men who are continuously busy and diligent have always been admirable members of the tribe; they are successful in modern society, but no one wants them to be kings — royalty must have a quality of repose.

The tiger sleeps a lot too, but he is not so open about it; he hides away in thick cover, he slinks through the shaded jungle, his stripes blending with the broken beams of sunlight. He lacks the apparent straightforwardness of the lion. He might be the wicked brother plotting for the throne; he will be a merciless tyrant if he ascends it.

Do not think me fanciful in all this. I believe these concepts go very deep within us and are part of the ancient history of man and color his attitudes today.

The other big cats seem small beside the lion and the tiger, but they are impressive enough in their own right. The leopard, or panther, and the cheetah, or hunting leopard, to some extent repeat the tiger-lion relationship which I have just described. As there are no tigers in Africa, the leopard takes its place — the Afrikaans for leopard is *tijger* — as the embodiment of savagery and the lightning strike. The cheetah, on the other hand, has something of the noble countenance of the lion and in its habits is sufficiently like a dog to have led some old naturalists to regard it as a link between the Felidae and the Canidae, the cats and the dogs.

And this brings me to another interesting point: our different attitudes to these commonest of domestic pets. Although the dog often shares the horse's honorific title of the Friend of Man, we never think of bestowing it on a cat, who is not a friend so much as a familiar. Of course, there are savage dogs and there are docile cats, living from one saucer of milk to the next, but the image of each which we have in our mind's eye and which has been handed down to us for generations is quite distinct. The dog has a bad as well as a good side: he may be a "mangy cur" or a pariah, right at the other end of the scale from the noble St. Bernard plodding through the snow with a little barrel of brandy round his neck; he is always in the role of a servant, whether he is unfaithful and treacherous or trusty and steadfast. Ages ago, when the whimpering jackals first crept closer to the campfires of the nomads, they bartered their birthright for a mess of pottage. But the cat has never gone down on his furry knees in allegiance. Take it or leave it, he says; I may be here today, tomorrow, I may stay for the rest of my life. But don't count on it, the world is wide. There are other hearthrugs and there is the wilderness where many of my relations are doing very nicely, thank you.

Many people keep both dogs and cats; some change from one to the other. For many years I would have called myself a cat-man and was never without one. In fact, I cannot remember ever living in a catless house. Michaela and I have five cats at present in our home in Kenya, and we have had at times as many as eleven, not counting kittens. When planning my first ambitious African expedition, I decided we should not go without a cat: a blue-gray alley cat named Pooka was my choice. Pooka survived two crossings of the Sahara, 42,000 miles of driving through African deserts and jungles, countless exploits and adventures. He contributed greatly to the morale of the expedition, he fathered blue-gray kittens all over the Congo, and became, on our return to the United States, a very celebrated cat.

At the moment dogs tend to rule our lives — our wonderful Rhodesian ridgebacks which have figured so often in our television programs recently. But the cats are supremely confident, and with reason, that the noisy, bustling dogs can never take their place.

One idea shared by many races of primitive man was that by killing a certain animal you could acquire the virtues or magical properties you believed it to possess. You might have to eat its flesh, or be smeared with its blood, or you might have to wear its horns or its skin. I suppose one of the best examples of this is the lion hunt of the Masai, that tribe of splendid physique which once dominated East Africa and whose riches are counted in the cattle they own. Their young men have complicated ceremonies of initiation, and the greatest test of the warriors, or *moran,* is to kill a lion, armed only with shield and spear but clad in their full imposing battledress. When they have tracked down their quarry, they surround him, chanting together to keep up their courage, and close in, sheltering behind their shields. The cornered lion finally charges a warrior, who takes the brunt on his shield, trying at the same time to stab the beast with his spear. The other *moran* join in, and when they have slain the lion dance round the body in triumph. The prize is the mane, which in the case of one tribe of Masai goes to the first man to seize the lion's tail; he is allowed to wear it instead of the usual headdress of ostrich feathers; another tribe gives it to the thrower of the first spear. Though lion hunting is now officially illegal, the *moran* sometimes break out and honor the old custom, by which, of course, they show their manhood against the fiercest animal they know and at the same time get rid of a dangerous enemy to their beloved cattle.

It is not such a far cry from the lion hunt of the Masai to the blooding of young riders which takes place after a successful fox hunt in the shires of England, and so I do not think it is far-fetched either to suggest that the big-game hunters who visit Africa and Asia to bag lions and tigers are partly moved by this sort of ancient belief. They would not admit it but, again, it does not seem a very long step from the Inca of Peru, killing a puma with the assistance of thousands of beaters, to a hunting safari by a wealthy American in Kenya today; and I dare say some of the qualities of a big carnivore would be very useful on Wall Street.

The subconscious belief is that by killing one of these animals you gain its courage, you prove your own and you have a fine trophy — a status symbol we should now call it — into the bargain. From the middle of the nineteenth century to the time of the First World War was the great period of the big-game hunter, but he was active long after that, and in the 1920's Sir Alan Herbert (A.P.H.) had a poem in *Punch* which suggested there might be another motive for a safari:

> *When Lady Jane refused to be*
> *The wife of Viscount Fiddledee*
> *He rose abruptly from his knee*
>   *And said, "Excuse this bungle —*
> *I think I will not stay to dine,*
> *There is a train at half-past nine;*
> *Tomorrow by the fastest line*
>   *I'm leaving for the jungle.*
>
>   *"Ho, varlet, run and pack my gun,*
>   *My passport pray discover;*
> *I mean to shoot some savage brute*
>   *To show how much I love her.*
> *Far off in India's poisoned swamps*
> *Some unsuspecting tiger romps,*
>   *Condemned to die;*
>   *And you know why.—*
>   *'Cos you won't marry me. . . .*
>
> *"I'll hunt him down on shiny nights*
> *With cunning telescopic sights,*
> *And, if the creature turns and bites,*
>   *As is his cruel fashion,*
> *I'll lie content and let him chew,*
> *A-thinking all the time of you;*
> *For what's the worst that he can do*
>   *Compared with hopeless passion?"*

The true motivation for many a hunting safari has been the hunter's need to assert his virility — whether to prove it to others or to prove it to himself.

Another, less destructive, form of safari grew up in the early years of the twentieth century into the '30's and will be always associated with the names of Cherry Kearton and the Martin Johnsons. The camera, first for still pictures and then for movies, began to take the place of the rifle. It was a slow process, of course, and often at first, I suspect, the animal was shot after its picture had been taken. Motor cars were still in their infancy and animals were not habituated, as they are now in national parks and reserves, to the sight of them; the Land-Rover and its relatives had not yet been invented. Once the first successful pictures had been taken, it became obvious that here was a sport far more exacting, dangerous, and rewarding than the easy triumphs of the shooting trip.

When I first went to Africa we had none of the portable cameras, the long-focus lenses, the wide apertures, the fast emulsions which are at our disposal today. To get a usable picture it was necessary to be very close to the animals, and this often involved the taking of considerable risks, but it gave a chance for prolonged observation — hours, sometimes, of cautiously following and watching an animal, until I got the perfect light and background for the picture I wanted.

I think it can fairly be claimed that the photography of the great mammals of Africa has been one of the chief causes of public interest in them and their conservation, and I am proud to have been one of the pioneers of the camera safari and the first man to bring the wildlife of Africa to the television screen with its enormous and appreciative audiences.

But there is a great deal to be done if we are to conserve the remnants of this wonderful wildlife, which is still shrinking fast. We must, for one thing, know much more about the habits of these decreasing species. When doing research for this book, I have been struck by the mystery that surrounds much of the life even of such well-known animals as the lion and tiger, leopard and cheetah, puma and jaguar. When we get to the smaller cats, the beautiful caracal and serval, which we have kept as pets, or the many interesting kinds that live in the jungles of Asia or the forests of South America, we come up against a wall of ignorance. "Nothing is known about its habits" — there are only the measurements of skins. Even the lynxes and wildcats that survive in Europe and North America, where there are thousands of keen naturalists, are not at all thoroughly studied, compared to many species of bird, for which voluminous textbooks, reporting on the results of much scientific research, are now available.

Naturally, if your only object is to trap or shoot an animal and make a trophy or a fur out of it, you will not learn much about its habits; and that is still very much the attitude in many parts of the world.

Besides the photographers, zoological gardens have done much good work, especially in recent years, to make people conscious of wild animals in the right way. I hope we are past the days of the "menagerie" for ever. A zoo now has a double function: it is a place of education where people can see in three dimensions the animals they only know in the wild from pictures; and it is a reservoir, a modern Noah's Ark, a living stockpile — use what metaphor you like — where rare species can be kept and bred when their natural habitat has been destroyed.

Fortunately, this does not yet apply to any of the animals I am writing about in this book, though at the present rate of decline the cheetah, already practically banished from Asia by all accounts, may not be able to hold its own in the wild much longer.

No zoo is complete without its cages of big cats. I do not myself much care for lions and tigers, leopards and cheetahs behind barriers, but many of those in zoos have been born in captivity and have never known freedom; and I think we must accept the view that they do not realize what they are missing. When a magnificent lion — and lions in zoos are often much more magnificent than they look in the wild — paces up and down, up and down his narrow cage, I hope he is not really seeing great herds of antelopes on the Serengeti Plains, but that he is simply fulfilling an inherited urge to take exercise and that he will be as happy when his next meal of horseflesh arrives on a trolley as if his harem of lionesses had just pulled down a zebra for him.

Many people go to zoos to gratify the feeling I tried to describe earlier. Here are great beasts of which our ancestors once went in terror — for there were lions in Europe not so very long ago — and now they are under the ignoble restraint of lock and key. But just suppose that a door was left open . . . Even when they are safe behind bars we cannot suppress a little *frisson* at the sleeping menace of their power. Perhaps one goes too close to another in its restless pacing and there are snarls and sudden, swift movements . . . No wonder feeding times for the lions and tigers are always announced beforehand and draw the biggest crowds of the day. Then we go out to the zoo's shop and buy little models for our children to play with.

Toys, in fact, have a lot to do with the imprinting on us of cat appeal, to use another scientist's word. If from our earliest days we are brought up with woolly lions and tigers, we lose that instinctive fear of them which a few babies always show — a relic of the days when the baby who screamed as a strange animal entered the cave was more likely to be rescued and to survive than one who welcomed the visitor. It is just as well that we do not live under the harsh laws of natural selection today. But the soft outlines and silly expressions of some nursery animals are a mockery of the real thing.

I am not writing anything about circuses because I dislike the sight of the big cats performing to the crack of a whip. I believe that the old, cruel methods of training are now a thing of the past. All the same, I am glad that acts with "tame" lions and tigers seem to be on the decline. Zoos we must accept and support as valuable institutions for education and conservation, but I hope that circuses will soon rely only on those animals that really are "friends of man."

So we have come back to the original theme of this first chapter: the peculiar relationship that exists between puny, versatile, imaginative man and the cat family, powerful, resourceful, perhaps imaginative too, but above all independent. In the chapters that follow I shall try to describe what is known of their lives and habits and tell you some of my experiences with them. There has been no book in English to include all the members of the Felidae since 1883, and that is now quite out of date and misleading. I am very honored to be the author of the first volume in the World Wildlife Series, and I can think of no more fitting subject than the group of wonderful and mysterious animals whose most famous member is the King of Beasts.

2. What Makes a Cat?

No FAMILY of animals is easier to recognize than the Felidae, or cats; whether we are looking at a lion, a lynx, or a small house cat, we are at once aware that they must be closely related. Even the curious Pallas's cat of central Asia (Plate 23), with its high-set eyes and muttonchop whiskers, is obviously one of the tribe.

Cats look quite different from dogs — from the outside. Yet if you were shown a headless skeleton, I think you would find great difficulty in telling whether it belonged to a cat or a dog. The bones of the toes are different because, as everyone knows, a cat's claws are retractable — that is, they are housed within the toes when not required. The main divergences between the two great families of carnivores lie in the skull.

Dogs hunt mainly by day and by scent, so their snouts are well developed; but most cats hunt by night and by sight, touch, and hearing, and it is no accident that their heads are on the same general plan as the owls', the nocturnal birds of prey. Sir Julian Huxley tells a story that illustrates this point. Many years ago a distinguished German diplomat was invited to a shoot at a great English country house. During one of the drives, a short-eared owl, which looks rather like a woodcock in flight, came over and was duly dispatched by the visitor. When his dog brought it in, he cried in surprise, "I have schot a schnipe mit face puschkats!"

It seems that the rather short, rounded skull is the best form for a night-hunter; like an owl, a cat can turn its head in all directions, and the skull is attached to the spinal column by especially strong muscles. All hunting birds and mammals have, like us, binocular vision so that they can focus on their victims precisely, whereas hunted animals have their eyes widely separated to cover as big a field as possible between them; they can literally see danger approaching out of the corner of their eyes. Cats and owls have

rounded faces and large eyes particularly adapted to seeing in poor light —
no animal, of course, can see in absolute darkness.

However, animals can hear in the dark, and research in the United States
has shown that some owls have wonderfully acute and accurate directional
hearing, enabling them to pounce on a prey that they cannot see at all. Cats
have well-developed earflaps, which are sound collectors; I do not know of
any research that proves they are capable of pouncing, by ear, with the same
uncanny precision as an owl, but this would not surprise me at all. Owls
operate from a perch or in flight; cats have to work on the ground and therefore have long and extremely sensitive whiskers, both over their eyebrows
and where the ends of a human mustache would be. These help them to
move silently through thick, dark cover, the whiskers gauging the width of
gaps in the vegetation. There is some argument about the effectiveness
of the cat's sense of smell; it seems to vary in different species.

To attain their round, compact skull the cats have had to sacrifice something. They have only thirty teeth, sixteen along the upper and fourteen
along the lower jaw. This is ten less than their more primitive relatives the
Viverridae, the family including the civets, genets, and mongooses, and
fourteen less than their remote ancestors possessed. All hunting animals
have developed teeth called carnassials to enable them to grip and tear flesh.
The cats' carnassials have evolved from an upper premolar and a lower
molar on each side and have a scissor action, the lower tooth working within
the upper. In spite of their name, the canines (dogteeth) are also better
developed in the cat family than in any other carnivorous group, which
allows us to claim that they are the most advanced of all the beasts of prey.

In compensation for their lack of grinding and chewing teeth, the big
cats have strong digestions, capable of dealing with chunks of meat swal-
lowed more or less whole. They cannot move their lower jaws from side to
side as we can; they have sacrificed mobility — which also helps when
chewing — to have a powerful masseter muscle; this moves the lower jaw
up and down, working within the wide zygomatic arches or cheekbones, and
enables the cats to grip their prey as in a vice.

Finally, in our tour of the cat's head, we may notice the rough tongue,
thickly coated with little horny projections, or papillae. They make a lick
even from a pet cat something of an ordeal; they have been adapted to rasp

or file flesh off a carcass, though their original function was as taste buds. Each genus of the cat family has a different arrangement of the papillae of the tongue.

I have described the skull of a typical cat first, because it is the family's most distinctive feature and contains several important pieces of specialized equipment. As I have already pointed out, the skeleton and, indeed, the whole body of a cat are remarkably like those of a dog. The bones are strong and solid, almost of the quality of ivory. The lion's backbone has seven vertebrae in the neck, thirteen in the thoracic region, seven in the lumbar and three in the sacral section; and there may be as many as twenty-six in the tail. Except for the lynxes, cats are all long-tailed animals. The small collarbone is set in muscle and not connected with the breastbone and shoulder blade as it is in man. This, I suppose, is another adaptation to increase the cat's sinuous ease of movement when hunting. The hind legs tend to be well developed — for springing and pouncing. The skin hangs very loosely, giving protection in fights. The number of nipples varies; the lion and lynx have two pairs, the house cat four.

The fur, or pelage, of the cats varies even within a single species. The tigers of Siberia, for example, have much thicker coats than those of the jungles of India. But markings throughout the family are really strikingly similar, consisting of stripes, blotches, and spots, with bands or bars round the tail, which often has a black tip. The ground color is usually a shade of light brown, tawny, or golden yellow, though some kinds have gray color phases. Some too, like the jaguar and ocelot in Mexico and the United States, have spots in the form of rosettes, or ocellations — irregular dark circles with lighter centers — which are very beautiful. Others, like the cheetah, have solid black spots. The lion, puma, and several smaller cats appear to be unmarked but show spots when cubs or as a faint pattern beneath the monochrome; and there have been several examples of lions in Kenya which retained their spots even when adult. So I think we can safely say that originally all cats were striped, probably along the back, or spotted, and that the single color is perhaps an adaptation to a life in the open, though President Theodore Roosevelt did not agree with this idea and occupied much of his interesting book on African game animals in attacking it.

The same patterning of stripes occurs again and again throughout the family, especially the markings on the head; the distinctive "tear-stripe," running out of the corner of the eye alongside the nose, links the largest tiger to the smallest tabby house cat.

Next to its head, its foot is the most specialized part of a cat. Cats, like dogs, walk on their toes; they are digitigrade, not plantigrade like flat-footed man. To this end they have large pads under their toes, as every dog and cat owner knows. The cats have five toes on their forepaws and four on their hindpaws. On the forepaw the second, third, fourth (the two longest), and fifth toes with their pads are arranged in a semicircle round the big central pad, which corresponds to the pad at the base of our toes, on which we rise when we want to run fast. The little first toe and its pad are raised off the ground altogether and can be used independently, as the cheetah does to grip its prey; it has disappeared on the hindpaw.

Not only do the soft pads make for quiet and easy movement, but cats have the additional ability to draw in their claws when not in use. The claws are retracted by an elastic ligament which acts on the last joint of each toe and bends it upward. When the animal is about to strike, the tendons of the muscles pull this last little bone down and the claw emerges instantly to do its deadly work. If your own cat will let you, you can examine all these details of the tiger's death-dealing mechanism in miniature on its pink and deceptively innocent paws.

Claws often split, and cats pull off the old sheath by scratching down trees or even in hard-packed soil; a new one grows below, just like our finger- and toenails. The pads under the toes are surrounded with long hairs, and lynxes have developed this into a wide paw which acts as a snow-shoe and is very useful in their northern home.

We have now seen the physical differences that separate a cat from any other animal. There are also differences of habitat and behavior. Apart from the lynxes, the Felidae are mainly animals of the warmer temperate and tropical zones, though there is some evidence that lions and tigers are invaders from the north, and several kinds, like the snow leopard and Pallas's cat, are adapted to live at high altitudes. The dogs, on the other hand, are, broadly, the carnivores of the north temperate zone. An important difference in behavior is that dogs are usually gregarious, living and hunting in packs, while the cats are solitary; even pairs do not stay together for long and the female often has to rear her family by her own efforts. Of course, we can at once think of exceptions: the lion with its prides, which sometimes number as many as thirty, and, among the dogs, the solitary brown fox of Europe.

But what about differences within the family of cats? We all know about the cheetah, or hunting leopard, which cannot fully retract its claws and looks almost ungainly, with its high haunches, until it bursts into its astonishing sprint. There are slight differences in its skull, too, and authorities have agreed for many years to put it in a separate genus. The genus is the group between the family and the species, the zoological unit, whose members normally breed true and with the members of no other species.

Some people still put all the other thirty-five cats into the one genus *Felis*; but there is a quite real difference between the biggest cats — tiger, lion, leopard, and jaguar — and the rest. The smaller cats, and the cheetah, have the usual connection between the larynx (the upperpart of the windpipe, our Adam's apple) and the skull by means of a number of small bones. In the case of the "big five" these hyoid bones are separated by a strong elastic ligament which provides the necessary sounding board for a full-throated roar; the other cats, in which the bones are linked, have to be content with a purr. So, as C. A. W. Guggisberg puts it, we can truly speak of "roaring cats" and "purring cats." A further difference is that while all cats have round pupils to their eyes, those of the smaller ones, as you can see in your own cat, contract to vertical slits.

The modern view, then, is to put the roarers in the genus *Panthera*. All the rest, except the cheetah with its own genus *Acinonyx*, remain in *Felis*, which you can, if you like, split into several subgenera on rather small points of detail. I give a list of the whole family and their scientific names in Appendix I.

So much for the cats of today, but what about their ancestors? When did this highly characteristic rounded head and stealthy form first appear on our planet? Authorities now believe that all our present carnivorous mammals (except, of course, those marsupials in Australia which have become flesh-eaters, like the so-called "cat" *Dasyurus*) are descended from the family of Miacidae which evolved within the Order called Creodonta during the

Eocene epoch, about forty to seventy million years ago. This period produced several catlike species but the first actual *Felis* did not arrive on the
scene until the Miocene — that is, between ten and twenty-five million
years ago. During the intermediate, Oligocene epoch cats, perhaps from
Asia, that reservoir of life, had reached Europe and America; and the
European *Aelurictis* is probably the direct ancestor of all our present-day
cats.

The famous saber-toothed tigers belonged to another group of early cats,
the Machairodontinae. Their upper canine teeth were so developed that
they met the points of the lower canines when the mouth was wide open.
A nearly perfect skeleton from America suggests that the saber-tooth was
rather larger than a lion, heavier, and more powerful altogether. No one
knows certainly how those terrible fangs were used. Were *Machairodus* (in
Europe and Asia) and *Smilodon* (in America) able to bring down elephants
and any other large land animal, or were they only, as some suggest, super
carrion-eaters, giant mammal vultures, using their teeth like a vulture's
beak to tear up carcasses? John A. Dow suggests that *Smilodon* preyed on
huge, slow-moving animals like the mastodon, mammoth, and giant ground
sloth, probably ambushing them and stabbing them to death without gripping. This is supported by evidence that *Smilodon* had extremely powerful
neck muscles but that those which close the jaw were relatively weak. At
all events, the survival of the saber-tooths for several million years suggests
that their methods must have been successful as long as they could find
suitable victims.

These monsters were at their peak of dominion over a million years from
our day; they vanished quite quickly, it seems, and the true Felidae took
their place. In America *Felis bebbii* of the Ice Age co-existed with the
faltering *Smilodon,* while in the Old World we find remains of the cave
lion, *Felis spelaea,* perhaps half as big again as our present lions. Early man,
of course, knew the cave lion well; its bones have been found in his caves,
and he drew its outline on their walls. Indeed, some authorities believe that
a small race lasted down to 6000 B.C.; but others think that this was really
a form of the existing lion, which had replaced its mighty relative. In
zoological evolution, as in human affairs, the race is not to the physically
strongest but to the most adaptable.

The modern natural distribution of the cat family covers almost all the land masses of Europe, Asia, Africa, and both Americas. There are no native cats in Madagascar, Australasia, or in many island groups round the world, but escaped domestic cats have "colonized" wherever man has carried them and, as we shall see later, they have taken a fearful toll of the local wildlife.

The domestic, or house, cat is recognized as a distinct species; there are thirty-five wild species, of which twenty-three are found in the Old World and eleven in the New, with the lynx common to the northern regions of both. Breaking them down into continents, we find that Asia has twenty-one cats, of which twelve occur on no other continent; Africa has eleven, of which three are special to it; South America has eleven also, with four special to it; and North America has eight. Europe claims four; the lynx, its own wildcat, island races of the African wildcat in the Mediterranean, and the leopard, which has a claw-hold in southeastern Russia.

Though Asia has the greatest selection of cats, I am going to write first about the cats of Africa, because that is where I live and work and because more is known about African lions, leopards, and cheetahs than about their relatives in Asia.

We have seen in this chapter the special features which go to make up a cat. Let us allow an old writer to synthesize them for us in the resounding prose of a former age: "No more complete example of a perfectly organized living being can well be found, than that supplied by a member of what has no inconsiderable claims to be regarded as the highest mammalian family — the family *Felidae*" (St. George Mivart, *The Cat*, p. 530). And the mammals, may I remind you, include man himself.

3. Cats of Africa: The Lion

We are in our Land-Rovers, by a waterhole, watching the drinking antelope and hoping for some slow-motion film of the graceful impalas making their prodigious leaps. Suddenly the herd, and the neighboring wildebeest, become nervous: they stop drinking, raise their heads, and we can see their lithe bodies becoming tense. Then they are off, bounding and springing like a corps de ballet, clearing the stage before the arrival of the principals.

But these are no prima ballerinas; these lionesses plodding on to the scene are more like two mothers returning from a long day at the seaside with their accompaniment of tired children — the young cubs, who are hardly able to walk without wobbling a bit. We know the signs; this is part of a pride coming back from a successful hunt and a meal by the light of the stars. The lionesses look at the fleeing impalas and wildebeest with interest, but they are obviously not hungry. The cubs took a long time over their eating and were reluctant to leave. The big male lion, the head of the family group, no doubt took his fill first and has now gone off ahead to lie up somewhere, probably with one or two of his latest and favorite wives, leaving the *hausfrau*'s to trail along behind and catch up with him.

The chances are that he has not gone far; after a heavy meal a lion is even more lazy than usual. He will be somewhere off the trail, in fairly thick bush for shade and protection, and near water. The lionesses will find him all right, and we will find him too, if we can stay with them.

Another lioness arrives, stalking along with her cub, but there is no sign of the "old man." The day advances and the sun high in the sky is shining down pitilessly. One by one the lions lie down to sleep. Surprisingly, for animals that live so much in the open, they suffer greatly from the heat, and the middle hours of the day are a torment to them. Some writers suggest this shows that lions did not originally inhabit tropical Africa but have come from farther north in quite recent times.

One lion cub still has the energy to visit the nearest recumbent lioness for a drink. Among the members of a pride mothering is quite communal; lions are united by an affection that is too seldom found even in human families, and they are remarkably tolerant of each other.

We move cautiously — lions are not distrustful of Land-Rovers — and meet still another lioness arriving, followed by a whole party of youngsters; and we feel we must be close to the "old man." Indeed there he is. As I suspected, he is like an Eastern potentate surrounded by his favorite dancing girls. He is not doing much to entertain them, and the two young ladies look decidedly restless and bored (Plate 2). It's all very well to be at the head of the top ten, but just sitting around listening to His Majesty's snores can be tedious. So one sneaks off, taking a chance on his not waking up. Will the other have the nerve to follow, or is she such a loyal soul that she will stick it out?

The lion stirs, but we cannot say that he looks particularly alert or ready to jump into action; he is just awake enough to pick a new position to go to sleep in. The second favorite goes off, and we do not notice any particular sign of resentment on the lion's part. And we too, having filmed our full of this domestic scene, withdraw quietly from the presence.

This is just one of many encounters Michaela and I have had with lion families since my meeting with a pride of twenty-five in the Ngorongoro crater on my first visit to East Africa, and it is because of their unique place in the cat family and in human admiration that I am devoting a whole chapter to the species in Africa. No one can now write about lions without acknowledging a debt to my neighbor in Nairobi, Dr. C. A. W. Guggisberg, whose book *Simba,* first published in 1961, is a mine of information on the distribution and natural history of his subject (much of it from firsthand observation) and on its place in human legends and affairs. Books have been written about the lion before, but none so compendious and the result of so much research. His bibliography includes well over four hundred titles that he has consulted, from the travels of Marco Polo to modern papers in scientific journals.

I mentioned above the theory, suggested by its apparently poor adaptation to very hot weather, that the lion may be a recent inhabitant of central Africa. This idea is supported, as Dr. Guggisberg points out, by the thick coat of the cubs and the mane of the male; he thinks it possible that the modern lion, when the cave lion had become extinct, retreated south out of a Europe covered with dense forest after the ice ages and found the open country it prefers in parts of Asia and, much more widely, in Africa.

We shall probably never get much nearer a solution of the lion's prehistoric distribution, but we do know that within the last few centuries it ranged in numbers over the whole continent, from the Mediterranean coast of Morocco to the Cape of Good Hope itself. It has over twenty names in different languages from the Swahili *simba* to the Zulu *ingonyama*. But the advance of civilization, above all improvements in the killing power of rifles, sealed its fate in much of Africa. The Moroccan lions, which seem to have been considered quite tame and harmless, were gradually banished to the Atlas Mountains and probably became extinct soon after the end of the First World War. Lions had vanished from Algeria twenty or thirty years earlier, about the time Alphonse Daudet wrote his story of the Provençal sportsman Tartarin de Tarascon, who, to back up his boasts, is forced to visit Algeria in search of a lion. After various ludicrous adventures, he succeeds in shooting a donkey in the dark. Sir Alfred Pease, who wrote one of the first monographs on the lion, was still optimistic about finding some there in 1892, so was delighted to see a fine maned specimen lying across the back of a donkey, its forepaws touching the ground on one side, its tail tuft trailing in the dust on the other. He jumped down from his carriage and asked where the lion had been killed. "Not dead!" replied the Arab who was leading the donkey. One of his companions tugged at a rope round its neck and "to my infinite surprise," says Sir Alfred, the lion scrambled off the donkey's back. It was an old beast but in good condition and had been blinded to render it "more tractable." The Arabs made their living by taking it round the villages where it was in demand because of its supposed power to exorcise evil spirits and cure illness. After Sir Alfred and his wife had looked at it, one of the Arabs gave it a whack with his stick; it climbed onto the donkey's back again and "appeared once more as limp and lifeless as a sack." The practical Pease, meeting it again in Biskra a year or so later, had its photograph taken in a natural setting outside the town.

Lions disappeared from Tunisia also about 1890. Farther east, in Libya and Egypt, they had been exterminated a century earlier, except for the occasional wanderer. A change in climate reduced the lions of the Sahara. As it gradually dried up and the herds of antelope left, the predators followed them, remaining only in the more verdant pockets, such as the oasis of Aïr, where they seem to have lingered into the present century. But they still occur right along the southern edge of the great desert and are quite numerous in parts of the Sudan, in southwestern Ethiopia and even in one area of Eritrea not far from the shores of the Red Sea.

The name Sierra Leone suggests lion country, but Dr. Guggisberg thinks it most unlikely they ever inhabited the rain forests and that the Portuguese explorer who bestowed it may have been prompted by the shape of a mountain or by the roaring thunder of the frequent storms. On the other hand, lions are found in suitable open habitats in most of the countries of West Africa except Liberia. This includes the former Belgian Congo, where I had my first and most alarming *rencontre* with a male lion when I was using a fisherman's hut as an improvised dark room.

The opposite side of the continent is of course the present stronghold of the African lion. Somaliland, once the happy hunting ground of the seeker after trophies, still has a strong population. Lions are not only found in all the national parks and game reserves of Kenya, Uganda, and Tanganyika, but are at large in the three countries, though not in their former numbers. Farther south, there are plenty in Northern Rhodesia and in parts of Portuguese East Africa; but they are scarce in Nyasaland; and in Southern Rhodesia are confined to the Wankie Reserve and the few districts where the game animals are still plentiful. Going west to Angola there were, at least before the troubles in that land, lions in the north. They thin out southward, though some are still to be found in South-West Africa.

Extermination of the South African lion population moved northward from the Cape, where there was a particularly fine race. The last lion in Cape Colony disappeared about 1850 and the last in Natal about one hundred years ago. But enough survived the determined settlers in the Transvaal to form a nucleus for Kruger National Park, and in parts of Bechuanaland they are relatively common.

There may be some tens of thousands of wild lions in Africa (there are about a thousand in the zoos of the world). These numbers may seem reassuring but we must remember that the lion is a predator dependent mainly on the big game animals and any further decline in their numbers could be disastrous to it. We are learning slowly that the conservation of wildlife cannot be divided into compartments: in the fast-changing world in which we live, all animals are vulnerable.

It seems inconceivable that the governments of the new countries of Africa will allow the lion, of all animals, to become extinct. Can you think of Africa without its lions? They were an important factor in its history when, with only primitive weapons opposed to them, they ranged at will over the open lands of the continent, striking terror into its villages, taking their toll of stock and exercising control on the herds of antelope and other wild game. Even at the end of the last century the famous Man-eaters of Tsavo were able to hold up the building of the Uganda Railway for nine months. Their victims included twenty-eight Indian coolies and many Africans, and they wounded one European before the redoubtable Colonel John H. Patterson finally put paid to their exploits and subsequently wrote a classic book about them. Trouble along the line from other lions continued for some years. One actually entered a shunted railway carriage where three Europeans were waiting for it but had fallen asleep, and killed a police inspector. The frantic telegrams sent by besieged stationmasters have been preserved and published. My favorite is:

> *Tsavo, 20.4.08. 23 hrs 25. The Traffic Manager: two down driver to enter my yard very cautiously, points locked up. No one can go out. Myself, shedman, porters all in office. Lion sitting before office door.*

And Tsavo has been in trouble as recently as 1955, when the Game Warden of the National Park received this message:

> *Urgent. Odeke narrowly escaped from being caught by lion assisted by ticket examiner two down date. All staff unwilling to do night duty. Afford protection. Confirm. Close for night working if no protection.*

Railway gangs all over Africa attracted man-eating lions, even as far south as the Transvaal; but this was a rearguard action. Today even the

King of Beasts is powerless against the juggernauts of modern technology.

Having enjoyed such a wide distribution over Africa, not to speak of its former range in Asia, the lion has been fair game for those zoologists called "splitters," whose penchant is for dividing up an animal into several species or at least into subspecies, often called geographical races. According to definition, the members of a species breed with each other and produce fertile offspring; if they succeed in mating across the species barrier and bear young, these hybrids, or mules, are generally infertile. This does not apply to subspecies, though if they are separated for long enough they may evolve into distinct species. No one today seriously suggests there is more than one species of lion in the world (*Panthera leo*), and obviously the different African populations of such a wide-ranging animal have little chance to become isolated. I suppose it is possible that if the Indian lion is allowed to survive it may eventually form a distinct species.

No less than twelve different races of African lions have been described, but Dr. Guggisberg does not consider that more than five or six are worth taking seriously. Two of these, the Barbary lion of North Africa and the Cape lion, are now extinct. Differences in size and the extent and color of the mane have been the main reasons for separating races, but it has now been shown that members of the same family may show sufficient variation to entitle them to belong to different subspecies!

So let us take a look at the physical characteristics of our hero and heroine. A male lion measuring more than ten feet from his nose to his tail-claw is quite exceptional. Colonel James Stevenson-Hamilton, who had data from some two thousand South African lions, did not record any that reached ten feet, and the average was less than nine feet; he has some scathing things to say about hunters who stretched skins; of one he wrote that "supposing its actual length to have been in the flesh as [implied], it must have looked in life rather like an enormous but much attenuated weasel." So we can say that nine feet is a good length for a full-grown lion and his lady will be about a foot less. Lions stand from two and one-half to three and one-half feet tall at the shoulder, lionesses being shorter but over-lapping these measurements. There is also a tendency to exaggerate weights. The great hunter Frederick C. Selous thought any male over 400 pounds was exceptional, and many are fifty to seventy-five pounds lighter, whereas lionesses may weigh well under 300 pounds, often given as the average figure.

I described the peculiarities of the cat family's anatomy in the previous chapter. The lion is distinguished by his massive skull — the record is, I believe, some sixteen inches by ten inches — and by the long tail with its tuft of black hair in which nestles the curious tail-claw, or spur, quite separated from the last vertebra of the tail and supposed, according to Dr. Guggisberg, to be supplied with nerves and blood vessels like a tooth. Its function has puzzled man for centuries: the ancient idea was that the lion used it as a sort of built-in goad to lash himself into a fury. Today we are skeptical enough to dismiss this picturesque theory but have nothing better to put in its place. There is no such mystery about the little dewclaws of the forelegs; they are used to retrieve lumps of meat when the lion takes too big a mouthful.

The lion has amber eyes, larger than a man's; the bristles of the "mustache" are in six to eight rows; the ears are tipped with black hairs which often betray an animal hidden in light-colored grass. Most adult lions and lionesses have elbow tufts of long hair. The lion's pulse rate is about forty to the minute and it takes a breath every six seconds.

Lion cubs are born with thick coats of fur, marked with pale gray rosettes; they have dark rings round the tail, which at first has no tuft. As they grow, the spots become fainter (see Plate 5) and usually disappear altogether, but some excitement was caused about thirty years ago by the supposed discovery of a race of spotted lions in the Aberdare Mountains of Kenya. An expedition was specially mounted to look for them. I think it is accepted now that the two beasts whose skins started the hunt were only varieties or mutants that may occur in any population. A better case can be made for the Cape lion as a well-defined subspecies: it seems to have been bigger than the African average, with a snub nose and a mane extending under the belly.

But the mane is an extremely variable character, in color, length, and extent; so is body color, with the suggestion that lions in desert areas tend to be lighter and those in forest areas darker, a distinction that could be brought about by natural selection comparatively quickly.

The lion's strength and agility are universally recognized. Jumps up to twelve feet in height and three times that in length are on record, though Dr. Guggisberg points out that the relation between the length of the fore-legs, the hind legs, and the spine shows that the lion is not as adapted to jumping as the lynx. Lions, especially when young, can and quite often do climb trees and rest in them (see Plate 5). In terms of pulling power a lion may be as strong as ten men, and his superb muscles ripple under the silky coat as he moves silently on well-padded feet, which may measure as much as eight inches across, his head held low. His traveling speed has been esti-mated at from two and one-half to four miles an hour — about the same as a walking man — but at times he trots and may break into a bounding gallop over grassland. He can easily travel twenty to thirty miles in a night. Lions can swim quite well but seldom do so for long distances.

Like the cat family in general, the lion depends mainly on sight to inform him of enemies and possible victims, though his vision is adapted to register moving objects. It has always amazed me that so many animals cannot recognize a motionless object, an ability which man, so poorly en-dowed physically in many respects, shares with the other primates. If you stand still a fair distance away, a lion simply is not aware of you — unless your scent betrays you, for the experience of Stevenson-Hamilton and many others have dispelled the old idea that the cats have virtually no sense of smell. I have often watched lions sniffing the air and feel sure that their noses are keen. They can follow the trail of a zebra unerringly, and even go after trucks loaded with carcasses. Their hearing is certainly keen, and this is another reason why they are able to pick out a moving animal as opposed to a stationary one.

Finally in the lion's physical equipment there is his roar, which is as much his hallmark as his mane, though it did not impress David Living-stone, the missionary and explorer, who compared it to the voice of the ostrich and said he could not tell them apart. But his is a lonely dart of criticism. To most people — hard-bitten hunters, professional zoologists, casual visitors — as to Michaela and me, it is the true voice of Africa. "The man who can listen to it without being stirred," wrote A. W. Hodson, "can have no romance in his being." The roaring lion lowers his head, arches his back and blows out his chest, sending a spurt of dust before him at each effort; but when lying down, he raises his head to roar. The lioness roars too, of course, but her voice does not carry so far. Zoo lions can be heard at least half a mile away over a city's traffic; in the wild the sound carries several miles.

Why do lions roar? Probably for much the same reasons as birds sing: to announce themselves and hence proclaim their territorial rights to other lions. And just as birds seem to go on singing, as we should say, for pleasure, once they have established their territories and secured a mate, so lions go on roaring. Their other noises — the grunt as they walk along, the growl of anger, the cough of fury, and the maternal mewing of a lioness — might be said to form a simple language. However, I think this is rather a misleading way of putting it. I believe that the calls of animals are uttered primarily as instinctive reactions to situations, not as "information," and that members of their species — and often of other species too — learn to interpret and act on them. The roaring lion is saying first and foremost to himself: "I am a fine fellow; this is my domain." Other lions learn that this means the territory is occupied and it will lead to a fight if they go on into it. I suppose it comes to much the same thing in the end, but my view seems to fit in better with our ideas of the evolution of animal behavior. Man alone has the power consciously to communicate, and look what a mess he often makes of it!

But I do not deny that members of the same species are very much aware of each other, and lions in particular. They are unique among the cats in living a group life in the pride, which is a loose association of individuals based on a family or families. Its numbers seem to vary according to the hunting opportunities: in some parts of Africa three or four is the normal pride, but in richer areas twenty or even thirty lions may hunt together. We saw at the beginning of the chapter what sort of social structure there may be in a pride: a king, or boss lion, at the top, attended by several wives and followed by others and their cubs. Young males often join too and eventually one of them may be strong enough to challenge the boss — or bosses, for sometimes two prides will link up.

When a boss or king is deposed, you sometimes find a most interesting situation: he joins forces with a younger male and acts as a sort of *éminence grise*, providing his experience in finding game while the other does the actual killing. But he is not above using his partner as a fall guy when necessary; James Stevenson-Hamilton tells of one great black lion, called Tshokwane by the Africans, who believed him to be the reincarnation of a headman with magical powers. Tshokwane eluded the hunter time after time but sacrificed several young associates in the process, letting them go ahead of him into danger. Bachelor clubs of males also form and similarly two or three lionesses may link up with their cubs; and though the prides have territories of a sort, they seem remarkably tolerant of other parties, except when the males are mating.

How then are we to square the easygoing, apparently liberal social life of the lions with many proved cases of terrible fights between them and of undoubted cannibalism? Most fights can be attributed to the mating season and are similar to those which occur among other loosely gregarious animals; the rutting season and battles of the red deer stags are a good example. Other fights arise over food in times of scarcity. Sometimes there seems to be no rhyme or reason in the killing and eating of a young lion or lioness by its companions. A lion in Nairobi National Park took to lion killing and was cured by castration, after which it lost its mane. Stevenson-Hamilton, whose lions in the Kruger National Park seemed particularly prone to cannibalism, found that these acts often took place when the animals were well fed. Can it be due to the overcrowding that may happen in a park or reserve? We are in deep waters here, for one of the great biological arguments of the day revolves round the possibility that animals regulate their own numbers before an actual food crisis occurs.

Apart from these fratricidal incidents, life today for a lion in a national park or reserve seems to be leisurely and pleasant. He has no natural enemies and has made his peace with man. One result is that he has once more become active by day as well as by night, and thus is much easier to watch. Old hunters and naturalists regarded the lion as nocturnal, but this seems to have been largely an adaptation to constant persecution by man, also a day-living animal.

Periodic hunts are now, as with leisured country gentlemen, the high spots of excitement in a lion's life. The general view is that a pride hunts with planned strategy and tactics, the lionesses doing the actual killing, the older lions cashing in on the proceeds, so to speak. Many writers have described this classic technique. When a herd of game is sighted, often by a waterhole, the younger members of the party make a detour, using all the cover they can find, until they are upwind of the prospective quarry, who catch the scent and bolt downwind, where the older lionesses are waiting for them.

Well, it may be so, but, as with lion language, I cannot help feeling that chance at first plays an important part in this supposed strategy: that the young lions often stampede the game accidentally, the cunning old ones taking advantage of this behavior and the pattern thus becoming established. Again, it comes to the same thing in effect, but my interpretation seems more in line with what we know of animal intelligence and its limitations. I was heartened to hear the other day from a friend in England who often takes quite a pack of dogs for a walk over his farm. When the young and inexperienced ones bolt a rabbit, an older bitch who knows the lie of the land anticipates which way it will run and lies in wait for it; but there is no evidence of prearranged cooperation between the yelping youngsters and the old hand.

When hunting alone a lion stalks upwind, using every scrap of cover with remarkable skill, and generally makes a final dash of about fifty yards over which it can attain a speed of perhaps thirty miles per hour — a little faster than a human sprinter. The fantastic speeds once attributed to a charging lion are now generally discredited. Only exceptionally will a lion run more than a hundred yards or so at speed, and an antelope or zebra which can keep ahead for that distance is usually safe for the time being.

There has been much argument about how a lion brings down a kill. Of course it depends on a number of variables: the size and strength of the prey, and the speed and angle at which contact is made. A single buffet will bowl a young antelope over. With a larger beast the lion very often gets a foreleg over its neck and throws it, the paw gripping the nose in such a way that the animal's neck is broken in the fall. The lion's hind legs usually remain on the ground for greater purchase, but the famous flying leap onto the victim's back does sometimes occur. Really big animals may be hamstrung from behind before being pulled down: a lion seldom attacks from in front, even when hunting quite small game; and with good reason, for there are quite a number of records of the attacker being severely injured and even killed by the desperate kicks or thrusts of various antelopes and buffaloes. Lions also have trouble with porcupine quills, which become embedded in their paws and may be a serious, even a fatal, handicap.

Having got the animal down, the lion usually finishes it off by biting at the throat; then the rest of the pride come up and the meal begins. The rasping tongue prepares the way for a neat disemboweling; the more tasty intestines — the green stuff ingested by antelopes may be important because of its vitamins — and organs are eaten and the contents of the paunch are dragged away and lightly buried or covered over. Where the ground is hard, the undertaker just goes through the motions. Lions as a rule eat their way forward from the hindquarters, swallowing great lumps of meat and skin, which is why they take so long to digest afterwards. Hyenas and jackals traditionally wait on the outskirts of the busy, gruesome scene, just as the lions lower in the pride order wait for the boss lion and his favorites to take the first cut. The vultures and marabou storks do not enter the stage until the lions have left, by which time there may be very little for them. Lions will charge vultures; I have seen one killed when too heavy with carrion to fly away quickly. Sometimes the pride visit the kill for several days before finishing the repast. They are quite indifferent to putrefying flesh and will, of course, eat animals killed by others; hence the use of baits to attract them, once to their deaths, now to be photographed and filmed.

How often do lions kill? Again, there have been all sorts of guesses and estimates. On one distinguished hunter's figures, the lions of the Serengeti Plains would account for more than 90,000 head of game annually! Dr. Guggisberg's observations in the Nairobi National Park suggest that one good-sized kill per lion every four weeks may be a reasonable allowance; that is, a total of about thirteen kills a year. Lions stoke up hugely after each kill and may each put away twenty to forty pounds of meat and skin. These estimates are based on animals living where the typical plains game — zebra, wildebeest, hartebeest, waterbuck, and smaller antelopes — is in good supply.

The range of food taken by the King of Beasts is almost incredible. Every creature from a termite to an elephant is on the list. Fish are scooped out of lakes and rivers, low-flying birds knocked down with a lightning stroke. Dr. Guggisberg also lists fruit, peanuts, rotten wood, grass, and garbage, including an African's shirt — minus the African. The typical prey animal varies in different regions. Wildebeest seem most popular in Kenya. Elsewhere, impala, zebra, even warthogs are favored. Some lions become monkey killers, preying especially on baboons. Domestic animals, of course, provide temptingly easy meat, and the remnant of India's lions feeds largely on the villagers' buffaloes. Where lions in Africa take to raiding stock, remarkable stories of their ability to haul their prizes over fences and zarebas are told; and I think it is well established that a full-grown lion or lioness can pull a donkey or a small native cow over a five-foot obstacle with little difficulty. They are also expert at forcing their way through defenses, as the Adamsons' Elsa did when she woke their publisher William A. R. Collins so alarmingly by getting into his tent and climbing onto his bed.

The lion's breeding cycle is distinct from the life of the pride. In East Africa mating generally takes place from February to April, and, as the gestation period is about 108 days, many cubs are born around July; but even in the wild there is no fixed seasonal pattern, and litters may appear in any month. The den is well hidden in thick bush or among rocks, not too far from water, and, as is usual among the cats, the mother looks after her young litter on her own. Our most accurate statistics on breeding come, of course, from lions in captivity. D. J. Brand has recently summarized 109 births in the national zoological gardens of South Africa. There was no definite seasonal distribution and, if cubs were removed when six weeks old, a lioness might have three litters within one year. Litter size varies from one to six; three is commonest, and the average between three and four, which agrees with observations in the wild and with the lioness's four teats. The sex ratio at birth is remarkably even: of 261 cubs in 84 litters, 131 were males and 130 females.

Cubs are born with eyes open or closed; they are about a foot long and weigh less than a pound. The first pelage is woolly and spotted, and there is no tuft to the broad, rather short tail. The first teeth erupt at about three weeks. For some weeks the cubs hide in the den while the mother goes hunting; they are very vulnerable and there is evidence of a big infant mortality in the wild. The hyena may well be an important predator at both ends of the lion's life cycle, first when it is a cub and finally when too old to defend itself. Two mothers or a mother and an "aunt" often join forces to hunt together. Once the cubs are able to leave the den the family may link up with a larger pride and the cubs may even meet their august father face to face. Usually he ignores them, but we have sometimes seen a lion show a tolerant interest in even quite small cubs.

So the cubs develop in the congenial environment of the pride. They are weaned at about six months and begin to join in hunts under their mother's guidance. Whatever may happen in zoos, wild lionesses seldom remate until the previous litter is nearly ready to "fledge." This testing time comes when they are about eighteen months to two years old, and all the severity of natural selection begins to operate on them. We have often seen thin and hungry cubs who have not yet mastered the skills of hunting for themselves. They must learn or perish. If they survive, they enter a carefree bachelor phase until reaching maturity at about four years of age, when they court or are courted and take up in their turn the duties of reproducing the species.

Few wild animals approach their possible life span. However lions may spin out their days in captivity, the life expectation of one that surmounts the trials of the first two years in the wild is scarcely eight more years. A ten-year-old lion or lioness is generally past its prime, though there are records of individuals living twice as long. The period when strength and speed are failing and teeth are worn is the danger period for man-eating. Nowadays this brings a speedy end, preferable to the nemesis that haunts old age in the wild: in the lion's case the humiliation of a ring of hyenas, waiting patiently until it is feeble enough for a sly attack. Better by far to die in battle with a younger rival — or am I guilty of anthropomorphism?

I have concentrated my account on the lion in his natural state, as we have come to know him during our many expeditions. But there is a whole lore and history about him in captivity. Man has kept lions and tamed them perhaps for three thousand years; they graced Egyptian processions and Roman triumphs. Modern menageries can be traced to the twelfth century and have been slowly transformed into the hygienic, scientific zoological collections of today. Generations of lions have been bred in zoos and never known the freedom of the plains. Also, man being the meddler he is, lions have been induced to mate many times with other large members of the cat family. The best known are "ligers" (lion × tigress) and "tigons" (tiger × lioness). As is often the case with hybrids, they are usually bigger than their parents. They were assumed to be sterile, and this has been confirmed by post-mortem on at least one male tigon. But about twenty years ago a fifteen-year-old female liger in the Munich zoo produced a female cub after being mated with a lion.

Even more complicated in origin were the litters resulting from the crossing of a lion with the female offspring of a male jaguar and a leopardess in the United States about sixty years ago; one of them was on show for a time at the London Zoo. Quite recently there have been successful crossings of leopard and lioness at the Hanshin Park Zoo in Japan. These curiosities, called "leopons," are of great interest to the student of animal behavior (see Plate 6). Dr. Hiroyuki Doi has made systematic observations on the two litters born in 1959 and 1961.

But lions in captivity cannot have the appeal of their fellows in the wild, and I would like to end this chapter by taking you with me to Africa again where Michaela and I are watching two prides that have joined forces to share a kill, giving us an unusual mixture of lionesses, young lions, and cubs of all ages and sizes. The boss lions are not on view. They do sometimes go off on their own, but we can see how well the lionesses control this motley party, even keeping the "teen-age" lions in order. They eat slowly, not wolfishly, and when the edge is off their appetites they go on licking the meat in sheer enjoyment. Little squabbles break out, but are soon over, and after the feast most of the lions just walk away and go to sleep. When I see this, I have a lot of sympathy for the view that sleep is the normal state of a big carnivore; it wakes only to hunt and feed.

The really exciting thing about this scene is that we two humans are able to watch it with no more concealment than a windshield. This would have been inconceivable a generation ago; already we take the new relationship between man and the big cats for granted and, more dangerously, the conditions under which it is possible. The national park is still an artificial sanctuary, existing only at the whim of governments. We must never relax our efforts until conservation becomes established policy in every African state and the lion can lie down in peace, if not with the lamb, then with the Land-Rover.

4. The Other Cats of Africa

As I was writing this chapter, about two hundred men, including one hundred and thirty policemen, soldiers, and inspectors of the Royal Society for the Prevention of Cruelty to Animals, with many schoolboys and a posse of tracker dogs, were searching woods on the edge of London — "Safari in S.E. 18" the papers called it — for an animal that might have been a leopard or a cheetah but ended up as a spotted Dalmatian dog. Such a hunt, which seems merely comic to people who have lived next door to these big cats in the wild for years as I have, illustrates all the same the excitement and glamour which they hold for the public in countries where they are only to be seen in zoos.

Yet between them and the lion there is a great gulf fixed, as I soon discovered when I sat down to write about them. "Leo" has exercised a special fascination for sportsmen, photographers, and naturalists; added to this, he could almost be called publicity-minded, and now that he is once more allowed to be diurnal his private life can be studied relatively at ease.

THE LEOPARD (Plate 7)

How different when we come to *Panthera pardus,* which actually has a much wider distribution than the lion, both in Africa and Asia, and manages to survive quite uncannily outside national parks and game reserves. In many ways the position of the African lion and the leopard in the cat family resembles that of the European wolf and fox among the dogs: the larger, social animal is scarcer than the smaller, solitary one. Though nearly extinct in Morocco and adjacent areas, and in most settled parts of South Africa, leopards are found throughout the rest of the continent, and inhabit the rain forests, from which the lion is absent.

The leopard relies on the thickest cover, in which it lies up during the day; this stealthy way of life gives it a great advantage. For many years I had only seen eight leopards in the wild and yet they prowled round our house in Nairobi and even killed two of our dogs within thirty feet of it. When I did see one, it just streaked across the plain or bounded through the high grass into concealment again.

At last, in the Serengeti Plains of Tanganyika, which is the best leopard country I know — scattered thorn trees where they can hide and watch the game come out at dusk to a river or waterhole — we came quite by chance on two leopards hidden in the grass. Apparently they hadn't seen us. It was a most exciting moment and led to others in the same area over the next year or two, as we gradually got better and better pictures. In my film *Below the Sahara* I showed a leopard taking a Thomson's gazelle down from its larder and dragging it away into the bushes. Now I wanted more than anything else to film the reverse process: a leopard dragging its kill up a tree. This habit is something special to it among all the big cats of Africa and Asia. It is done, of course, to protect the carcass from hyenas and other scavengers, so that it can be devoured at leisure.

Eventually, while we were filming a reedbuck, we saw a leopard taking quite a different interest in our subject. The buck escaped and we thought our chance had gone, but we were wrong. The leopard had already made a kill and had left it lying on the ground while diverted by the reedbuck. Now it began to drag the carcass, a topi antelope, young but obviously already much heavier than the leopard, toward a tree. To our delight we saw it was being followed by one, then two cubs, who playfully ran alongside, trying to take bites out of the topi and making the big one growl in remonstrance. The cubs disappeared in the long grass, and the leopardess, for such we presumed she must be, reached the foot of the tree and looked up . . . The camera ran out of film! By the time it was reloaded, she was thirty feet aboveground with the topi, its legs dangling on either side of a branch; she was panting with the terrific exertion but was apparently quite indifferent to us. Calmly she removed a thorn that was in her way and instead of tearing the carcass began to pluck the hair, pulling it out in tufts at the spot where she would no doubt start to eat later; but it was half an hour before she began her meal. Every time I run through that film I am convinced that a leopard in a tree is completely unconcerned with human spectators, because it believes it is invisible to them.

Cats of Africa.   Plates 1, 2

facing page 22 (Plate 1): Cheetah
with gazelle

top left: Serval
center left: Caracal eating hare
bottom left: Cheetah with gazelle

Lioness yawning

So, while we have our leopard up a tree, what does it look like? Male and female are similar and average about seven feet in length, of which three feet may be tail. There is great individual variation, with length up to eight feet, and there is even a record from Tanganyika of nine feet seven inches. Leopards stand from two feet to two feet four inches at the shoulder, just overlapping the smallest lions. The weight range has been given as from 120 to 180 pounds, with exceptional animals up to 200 pounds, but I think this must refer to hill-country leopards, which are generally larger. Colonel Stevenson-Hamilton's Transvaal weights show that a full-grown male there rarely exceeds 100 pounds, with females twenty to thirty pounds lighter; Carl Akeley's leopardess (see p. 34) was only eighty pounds.

The leopard's eyes are greenish, with round pupils; the record skull is about twelve inches by six inches. The generally yellow coat, with the rather smudgy rosette spots, and the lighter belly are well known to every zoo-goer. The "black panther" — Kipling's Bagheera — is merely a black mutant of the leopard, fairly common in India but very rare in Africa. As with the lion, the splitters have done their best to divide the leopard into subspecies. There is supposed, for example, to be a small race in Somaliland and a large, pale one in the Caucasus, but I doubt very much whether the variation between these races is any greater than between individual leopards from the same area, with the exception that animals from the hills do seem to be bigger than those in low country.

When you try to discover what other writers, naturalists, and sportsmen have said about the leopard, you find a great many anecdotes of pursuit and combat, usually resulting in its death after a desperate fight — for it is the fiercest of the big cats, the only one that will sometimes attack man without provocation. But about its general natural history there is remarkably little on record, though its hunting methods are fairly well known. First there is the stalking approach, similar to the lion's, but carried out perhaps with even greater stealth and ending in a short final spring or dash. The other method, which may be more generally used, is the ambush: the leopard lies up in cover near a game trail, or on the bough of a tree overhead, and pounces on its prey. It kills by biting through the jugular vein or crushing the vertebrae of the neck in its powerful jaws, and then licks up the blood before pulling the carcass away into concealment. Like the lion, the leopard removes the contents of the paunch and buries them. Then it starts its meal on the edible organs. After that it begins on the face of the prey rather than on the hindquarters as the lion does. It is a more elegant feeder than the lion, though it does swallow lumps of meat and skin. After its first meal, the remains may be hauled up a tree to a larder in the manner already described.

The leopard slakes its thirst before retiring to sleep and digest, but it will return again and again to a kill, though not necessarily on successive nights, and it is no more put off by "high" flesh than a lion is. Leopards, however, are not so fond of carrion they have not killed themselves and only eat it when very hungry. They take a great variety of game; and though they cannot tackle animals as big as a lion can, they kill many of the smaller antelopes and occasionally attack female kudu and waterbuck. As Stevenson-Hamilton wrote: "The leopard is liberal in his ideas as to diet and devours impartially almost any warm-blooded creature which he can overcome, be it mammal or bird"; one even had a go at the colonel's gray stallion. Like lions, they sometimes run into trouble from porcupines although they do not seem to suffer so much from quills in their paws. In India their appetite for dogs is famous. African leopards also snatch them at night but will not take on large dogs in the daytime if they can avoid it. I do not think they are habitual fishermen. However, I believe most members of the cat family take fish from time to time, usually from very shallow water.

Leopards do not always have it their own way with prospective victims. If they are surprised by a horde of baboons when on the prowl they usually retreat, for there are cases of their being surrounded and killed. Wild boars and male bushbuck, as well as lions and crocodiles, of course, are credited with killing leopards. They in turn will kill jackals and servals and are perpetually at feud with hyenas, which, in a pack, can drive a leopard off a kill. Sir Alfred Pease saw a leopard leap a thorn fence to take a sheep from a Somali encampment, only to be robbed of it by the hyenas waiting outside. It is said that a trapped leopard will not gnaw itself free as many other carnivores do; it can be caught by a single toe.

But a leopard at bay is braver than a lion, which makes the famous feat of Carl Akeley, American naturalist, taxidermist, and sculptor, the more remarkable. He was on his first visit to Africa in 1896 when he was attacked by a female leopard that knocked his rifle flying and seized his right forearm in her mouth. "This," he wrote,

not only saved my throat but left her hind legs hanging clear where
they could not reach my stomach. With my left hand I caught her
throat and tried to wrench my right arm free, but I couldn't do it
except little by little. When I got grip enough on her throat to
loosen her hold just a little, she would catch my arm again an inch
or two lower down. In this way I drew the full length of the arm
through her mouth inch by inch. Finally, when it was almost freed,
I fell to the ground, the leopard underneath me, my right hand in
her mouth, my left hand clutching her throat, my knees on her
lungs, my elbows in her armpits, spreading her front legs apart so
that the frantic clawing did no more than tear my shirt.

Eventually, by this combination of forcing his right hand down her throat
and gripping her with his left, Akeley succeeded in strangling the leopardess, while the pressure of his knees crushed her ribs. But even when she was
dead there remained the probability of blood poisoning from the tooth
wounds. So antiseptic was pumped into them "until my arm was so full of
the liquid that an injection in one [wound] drove it out of another." Akeley
recovered and became a pioneer of conservation up to his death in 1926.
His exploit was repeated more recently by Gilbert Sauvage, who was also
badly mauled in a battle. An onlooker with a rifle was unable to help,
perhaps because he was afraid of hitting the man in his excitement.

In Africa leopards have a reputation as man-eaters almost as bad as that
of lions. It is said that the local inhabitants are often to blame. Superstitious about deaths in the kraal, they drive the aged and seriously ill into the
bush, where, of course, it is easy for lions, leopards, and even hyenas to find
and kill them. So the habit forms and the animals lurk round the settlement in hopes of more easy meat.

Maurice Ryan has described his experiences "at the unforgettable Kilo-
meter 879 siding on the Benguela Railway" in Angola. A village headman
asked help in saving his people from an evil spirit that was attacking and
killing them. Soon afterwards one of Ryan's servants was attacked by a
leopard in daylight, and, though he scrambled into a tree he was clawed
in the leg and died of blood poisoning. Next the man-eater forced its head
between the poles of a hut and seized a boy by the arm, but was frightened

off when a railway ganger fired his shotgun. A few nights later it attacked a group who had settled in to sleep round their dying campfires, and before the leopard escaped by a twenty-foot leap over a seven-foot truck it had wounded two men, one of whom refused to see a doctor and also died of blood poisoning.

The next incident had tragicomic touches. A newly arrived locomotive engineer from England was eating his supper in his hut with his fox terrier beside him when the leopard sprang into the room, skidded on the smooth cement floor, and sent the man, the dog, and the furniture flying. Recovering quickly, it seized the terrier and disappeared. Soon afterwards Ryan saw a leopard cross the track in broad daylight, but he was unarmed. Another death followed in the village, then a Portuguese foreman lost all but one of a dozen sheep in a single raid and Ryan persuaded him to let the survivor be used as a live bait with a camouflaged pit between it and the entrance to the pen. The leopard duly arrived that night, forced its way through the roof of the pen, and crashed into the pit. By the time Ryan had run up and climbed on top of the pen it was out again and ready to spring at him. He fired his rifle one-handed, as if it were a revolver, and shot the animal through the brain. That was the end of the evil spirit.

I have quoted this account at some length because it is so full of incident and illustrates the extraordinary boldness and persistence of the confirmed man-eater and stock-raider. Quite similar stories could be duplicated many times over. There are even reports of whole villages being so persecuted that they were deserted by the terrified inhabitants.

Even when a death is not actually involved, the leopard seems to be the center of strife. François Edmond-Blanc was photographing in the Serengeti game reserve, which I have already described as wonderful leopard country, when his party came on a huge one lying on a rock at the foot of a spreading tree. They were able to get within thirty yards in the car and take a number of pictures before settling down to the unusual experience of watching a resting leopard in broad daylight. After half an hour the animal suddenly scented or saw something, jumped down off the rock, and crouched in the low vegetation, looking up from time to time in the same direction. At last the party in the car also saw the head of a lioness obviously intent on the spot where the leopard was hiding. She began to stalk until she was only five yards away, then she "pounced upon him with a terrific growl." The leopard avoided the attack, jumped back onto the rock, then up in the tree, the lioness following agilely and twice only just missing her strike. The leopard reached the top of the trunk in a couple of bounds and continued climbing into the small branches "that would have been fitter to bear little birds." The lioness tried to reach it, but had to give up and slid back to the ground. She stared up at the tree for a few minutes before galloping away to some rocks where she no doubt had cubs — the reason for her attack, which Monsieur Edmond-Blanc was able to document with photographs.

As well as being such agile climbers, leopards are good swimmers. Stevenson-Hamilton said they often used the islands in the Sabi River as lying-up places during the day, especially in the winter, when many females have small cubs. Leopards will haul kills as big as impala through shallow water, pulling them by their necks as lions do. On land their gait also resembles a lion's but they probably range less widely.

The leopard's usual call is a sort of coughing grunt; it is often repeated several times, when it sounds rather like a saw going through wood. The grunt of alarm or anger is lion-like but less powerful. Though the structure of the throat would seem to permit it, I do not think there is any record of leopards roaring. On the whole they are rather silent animals.

Both Stevenson-Hamilton's wide experience in South Africa and D. J. Brand's recently published records from zoos suggest there is no fixed breeding season in the wild or in captivity, though in South Africa litters tend to be born in spring or winter. The gestation period is 93 to 103 days and Brand's litters were from one to three, averaging 1·75. In the wild, though two cubs may be weaned at about six weeks, usually only one survives to attain full independence at eighteen months or two years of age. Except for the association of the leopardess with her family, and for her brief courtship period, leopards are solitary, though several may be found hunting in an area where game is plentiful or stock easy to raid.

In spite of their traditional antagonism, lions and leopards are alleged to hybridize occasionally in the wild. In the preceding chapter I mentioned crosses with lions in captivity. There is also the curious case of the animal reared about 1900 in Carl Hagenbeck's Tierpark by a fox terrier bitch. It was apparently the survivor of three sets of twins borne by a leopardess to a male puma. It had male characteristics, a long tail, and was intermediate in coat color and pattern between its parents, having pale leopard-like spots on a puma ground, but it was only half their size.

It is by no means impossible to tame and make a pet of a leopard, provided it be raised by hand and constantly handled, almost from birth, by its human foster-father or foster-mother. Michaela had a famous leopard, Tshui, the hero of her book *Leopard in My Lap*. Tshui was wonderfully tame, and lived in our garden in Nairobi. He was never known to use his claws or his magnificent fangs, even though he was fond of springing unawares upon visitors and bowling them over — a game which more than once resulted in more consternation than amusement. We could never quite convince our friends and neighbors that Tshui's heart held no malice, and that the ferocity with which he sometimes stalked visitors was all in fun. Our cheetah pets were always more popular.

THE CHEETAH (Plates 1, 2, 8)

All reasonable people in Africa sleep during the hottest hours of the day and we are no exceptions, taking a nap in a hide when we are on an expedition. One day, when Michaela woke, I had a surprise for her — a cheetah was standing a few feet away, in easy photographic range. Now, though cheetahs are like lions in being active by day, they prefer the early mornings and evenings. To see one like this was quite unusual, and its presence was no doubt the explanation for the uneasiness we had noticed earlier among the game animals. The cheetah had obviously been resting like us and was now thinking about an evening hunt. Then a second cheetah appeared, moving effortlessly through the long grass; they are less solitary than leopards and often go about in pairs or small groups.

It is strange that cheetahs should look so beautiful in motion when they are really rather ill-proportioned — they are too rangy, their bodies seem to hang between legs too long, their heads are much too small, out of scale with the rest of the animal. Also, there is something sad and mournful about a cheetah's face, because of the two heavy black tear-stripes running on either side of the nose from the corners of the eyes to the corners of the mouth. When you see cheetahs in action you forget all about the apparent lack of proportion, which, of course, is really adaptation to a highly specialized hunting technique. In a fraction of a second their supple bodies stiffen like steel and they can break into a sprint which may for a moment reach sixty miles an hour, making them the fastest mammal on earth — faster than any antelope.

These cheetahs were obviously hunting together; they could have no pre-arranged plan, yet each seemed to know what the other would do. I think this comes from long experience and not from any intuitive intelligence. A third animal joined them, looking as if it had just covered an area of country in vain. The trio separated to search and we could not follow them.

Having sighted game, the cheetah begins its stalk like a lion or leopard, crawling upwind, belly to the ground, until it is within a few hundred feet of its prey. Then comes the famous lightning dash ending with a blow at the victim's hind legs, or a spring at its throat or onto its back, bringing hunter and hunted to the ground. Though neither teeth nor claws are as strong as a leopard's, they do not easily relax their grip, and death usually comes from a bitten jugular vein or windpipe.

Nothing causes so much controversy among naturalists as the speed that animals can attain, and since cheetahs have been used as "hunting leopards" for hundreds, perhaps thousands of years because of their pace, they have attracted quite legendary attributes. It is only recently that precise timing has been attempted. The comparatively moderate rate of 100 yards in four and one-half seconds, or about forty-five miles per hour, has been recorded with tame cheetahs in Britain — but in Florida seventy miles per hour is claimed! As I have already said, I believe that, at the peak of its sprint and on suitable flat ground, a cheetah may touch sixty miles per hour, which is quite fast enough, given the element of surprise, for it to be on its quarry before the victim itself can get into its stride. When pursued by Land-Rover in the open, cheetahs show little fight and can easily be run down and captured.

The cheetah is a milder and more gentlemanly character than the leopard, but I am afraid his table manners leave much to be desired. He tears open the belly of his kill and pulls out the contents, and does not bother to cover it up. Heart and kidneys are usually left in position and eaten first. Then he tackles the cartilage of nose and ears, perhaps the tongue, and the meat of face and neck before working along the carcass via the ribs to the hind-quarters, leaving the liver and the forequarters to the last. It is curious that most if not all carnivores have such characteristic methods of eating their prey that an experienced observer can guess at once the identity of the killer by casual examination of the remains of a carcass. A cheetah's work is particularly easy to recognize by, as Stevenson-Hamilton put it, "the slipshod, dirty way in which the carcass has been butchered; the prey is generally "eaten where killed, and not dragged away to shelter."

The cheetah's hunting methods are best suited to reasonable daylight, which accounts for its dawn and dusk activity. In Africa its normal fare includes a variety of the smaller antelopes and the young of larger species. Though their table manners may be open to criticism, cheetahs do not normally eat carrion and therefore seldom revisit their kills. There are occasional records of cannibalism. Stevenson-Hamilton knew two cases of males fighting to the death and the conqueror then eating part of his vanquished foe; in one instance a reedbuck, evidently the bone of contention, was left untouched. Dog may not eat dog, but cat is not averse to cat if provoked sufficiently.

The distribution of the cheetah is also governed by its habits, though it would be more correct to put it the other way round: cheetahs are big cats that have become adapted to life in savannah or open grassland. They were once found all over the continent in such country but are now very much confined to parts of East, central, and South Africa.

The long, sinewy legs and powerful hindquarters at once proclaim the cheetah as a specialist, but specialization extends to points of detail. The "free" claws in the rather splayed toes give a better grip of the ground for speed, while the actual pads — sharp-edged under the toes, compressed under the middle of the paw, horny and pointed at the carpal joint — have been developed to allow quick braking and changes of direction. It is not in fact true to say that the claws cannot be retracted: they are, when necessary, but they are not protected by sheaths of skin as are those of other cats and become blunted with use. The dewclaws of the forelegs are more strongly developed than in other cats and play an important part in holding on to the prey. The skull too has evolved away from the typical cat shape. It is relatively small (compare that of the greyhound with other dogs) and its high dome with the raised eyesockets enables the cheetah to peer over low cover when lying flat on open ground. The nasal passages are enlarged to give an oxygen boost during the great effort of the final sprint.

Sacrifices have been made in the jaws, which are rather short. The canine teeth are noticeably smaller than those of the leopard and the carnassials do not have cusps on the inner edges, and therefore are not so effective in crushing. The whiskers, whose length is an adaptation for hunting in thick cover, are shorter than the leopard's.

The cheetah's coat is usually a rather reddish yellow and the spots on it are solid black, immediately distinguishable from the rosettes of the leopard. This spotted coat is supposed to be "cryptic," helping to conceal the animal in its preferred open habitats, but I must own to being a heretic in these matters. To me no animal is more conspicuous than the striped zebra, often quoted as a remarkable example of concealing coloration.

Another special feature of the African cheetah is the neck crest, or ruff, common to both sexes. Asiatic cheetahs only show it in the winter coat. Though in general I think the cheetah's markings are less variable than those of most other cats, there occurs in Rhodesia the strikingly beautiful pattern whose possessors have been dignified by the title "King," a translation of the scientific name *Acinonyx rex,* bestowed when it was thought a new species had been discovered. King cheetahs are distinguished by long black stripes down the back, and by long bars, blotches, and spots of all shapes and sizes on the flanks, and black bars also run down the tail.

Photographs of one trapped by Africans in the Umvukwe Range of Southern Rhodesia, northwest of Salisbury, in September 1926 caused a sensation when published in *The Field.* A local authority, Major A. L. Cooper, considered the animal might be a hybrid of cheetah and leopard, but the skin was shipped to Britain as of "an undescribed species of cheetah." It then emerged that another had been killed in the Siki Reserve, twenty-five miles south of Salisbury, in May 1926 and Cooper was told they were fairly common — two had been shot in the Bikita district in June 1925. They were also called "Mazoe leopards" and "African ocelots." Eventually R. I. Pocock of the British Museum of Natural History decided that they were only a remarkable mutation of the cheetah; few have been reported in recent years.

The female cheetah is usually a little smaller than the male. The height at the shoulder is from two and one-half feet to three feet — taller than a leopard; the length of head and body combined is about four and one-half feet, with the tail another two and one-half feet. The African record is a total length of seven and three-quarters feet. The record skull is only eight and one-quarter inches by five and three-quarters inches — considerably smaller than the leopard's. The weight range in East Africa is from 100 to 140 pounds.

Cheetahs have a repertoire of expressions, growling, snarling, spitting, mewing, and purring almost like a house cat, but their most unusual noise is the birdlike chirp, as it is described by most writers.

The two to four kittens may be born at any time of the year. They arrive in the world blind and are covered at first with long, rather soft, blue-gray hair on their backs. The rest of the body, tail, and legs is tawny brown, with solid dark spots. I think they are the most beautiful of all young cats, and I shall never forget the day I received a telephone call asking, "Mr. Denis, would you like to adopt four wild cats?" We did not want any wild cats, but I was afraid they would be destroyed if I said no, so I drove the seventy miles to the farm where they had been found — and there were four precious cheetah kittens.

We experienced no great difficulty in raising them, though they are supposed to be subject to rickets in captivity. By chopping up chicken feathers and adding them, with bone meal, calcium, and cod-liver oil, to the kittens' meat we hit on the right antidote. The young cheetahs lived in a big enclosure with plenty of sunshine and room for exercising to their hearts' content, and they grew up strong and healthy. Mrs. Mary Holdstock has also described how she took over three cheetah kittens about six or seven weeks old and in very poor condition. She fed them at first on creamy milk with sugar and cod-liver oil out of a miniature bottle and they thrived. After having them for a week, she started giving mincemeat: at two months they had the appetite of a full-grown house cat but too much meat made them constipated.

She comments on their very sharp claws. At this age it has often been noticed that cheetah kittens can climb quite well. Two kept by Stevenson-Hamilton ran up the walls of a large wire-netting cage "with the facility of ordinary cats and could even cling to the roof." It is a different story when they grow up, though — cheetahs will not accept the fact that they are bad climbers. They insist on behaving as if they were leopards: graceful as they are when racing, they look very clumsy in a tree. A sloping trunk has an irresistible attraction for them, and when they do get up a short way they are as proud as peacocks and expect to be complimented. In the wild, cheetahs sometimes try to climb trees in an emergency. This and their ability to climb when young strongly supports the idea of their evolution away from the more typical cat physique and attributes.

Tame cheetahs show some desire for affection. Michaela's particular favorite would seize her hand or wrist until she turned all her attention to him. Cheetahs in Africa are frequently kept as pets, and generally believed to be free of the "unreliable" streak that is supposed to be found in other big cats when domesticated. I am not in full agreement with this optimistic view, though I have kept a number of them at various times. When I lived in the United States I took one to a cinema, where it became infuriated by a tiger on the screen and caused me great embarrassment. I shall describe more about the use of cheetahs by man in the next chapter, since it is in Asia that it attained its highest development.

THE CARACAL (Plates 2, 8, 9)

Like its larger relatives, *Felis caracal* was once distributed over the more arid parts of southern Asia and Africa, where it is still found fairly widely, though probably most commonly in the south of the continent. I would feel inclined to back a claim that it is the most beautiful member of the whole family. When we were selecting a colored cover for the first number of *Animals* Magazine it was the close-up of a caracal's head that I chose in preference to a lion, tiger, leopard, or cheetah. To me it epitomizes the lithe, compact strength of the cat tribe. The pointed ears with their tufts of black hair add an original, slightly diabolical touch. The eyes too are a baleful pale green-yellow, and the whole animal gives an impression of magnificent ferocity, earning it the Swahili names of *Simba mangu* or *Simba kali,* "little lion" or "fierce lion."

The tufted ears, which are black behind, and the short tail and strong legs suggest a close relationship with the lynx group of more northern latitudes; but the coat is uniformly rufous brown above, not striped. The chin, throat, and underparts are white, with indistinct reddish spots on the belly; there is a dark spot above the eye. The head and body together are twenty-six inches to thirty inches long, the tail nine to ten inches and the animal stands sixteen to eighteen inches at the shoulder. The ears are about three inches long to the tip of the tufts. The young resemble the adults and are born in litters of one to three according to D. J. Brand, with an average of two. There are records of four kittens in the wild, where the peak of breeding — at least in eastern Transvaal, where Stevenson-Hamilton studied it — is in July and August. The den may be in a tree cavity or down a disused ant-bear hole in the ground.

The haunts of the caracal are mainly in open country, sometimes mountainous, sometimes bush-covered. It lies up most of the day in concealment, though Stevenson-Hamilton saw one out at 8 A.M. on a hot summer morning and mistook it for a steinbok. As caracals are largely bird-eaters, they must be active when their prey is roosting and Stevenson-Hamilton found remains of the powerful tawny and martial eagles which had been killed by them. They also take a great variety of small mammals, including antelopes like duiker and steinbok and young impala and reedbuck, with sheep and goats when they get the chance. I have not watched them hunting myself, but they evidently stalk and pounce like leopards. They are also good climbers and take to trees when pressed, which unfortunately makes them easy to shoot. But they are a match for most dogs when driven to bay, spitting and growling like other cats. Their normal call is a leopard-like cough.

The caracal has a reputation for wildness, but Raymond Hook gave us a young one that calmed down remarkably when given milk to drink. It may be a question of catching your *Simba kali* young enough and then of the right diet, because there are cases of caracals becoming perfectly tame. Ours had fits of wildness which I remember the Boran people, whom we were visiting at the time, found very distressing, because they have such excellent manners themselves. Still, a saucer of milk had a magical effect.

THE SERVAL (Plates 2, 10, 11)

The next largest species, though it is much more lightly built than the caracal, is *Felis serval*, which is confined to the African continent. Its ears are also its most noticeable feature, for they are large, rounded, and so wide at the base that they almost meet on top of the head like the ears of some species of bats. This suggests a highly developed sense of hearing, the ear flaps acting as parabolic reflectors. Indeed, my friend Raymond Hook, who has made a study of them both in the wild and as pets, believes that they hunt mole rats at night by listening for their burrowing noises close to the surface.

The serval is long-legged, standing about twenty inches at the shoulder. Head and body together measure about three feet, the tail adding another nine to twelve inches. An adult weighs about thirty-four pounds. Two forms of coat pattern occur, the typical serval (tawny with black spots, elongating to stripes on neck and shoulder) and the servaline (which has small black spots finely distributed over a tawny-gray ground — they were once considered to represent distinct species). The fur of the underbody is long and thick, and almost white; the tail has a black tip and black rings; and the prominent ears are white inside and black behind, with a white spot. A black-coated form occurs; it has been reported in Kenya on the moorlands at 10,000 feet. Raymond Hook has one as a pet.

The serval inhabits medium cover in rather broken country of small hills or foothills, lying up in bush, long grass, or reeds — often near water — during the day and hunting by night. As an expert climber it is able to stalk birds at roost in trees but it also preys on ground-living species like guineafowl and francolins, as well as on small mammals up to the size of young duikers and steinbok. Two have been seen near a ewe in labor, presumably with the worst intentions. But, unlike the caracal, it is no match for quite a small dog.

The repeated cry of the serval, variously rendered *how how how* or *mwa mwa mwa*, may be heard at night; when cornered it spits and snarls like a house cat. In South Africa breeding takes place at the end of the winter, about three kittens being born in the abandoned hole of a porcupine or ant bear.

We have kept tame servals, though they hardly deserve the adjective. They are playful, fascinating pets as long as you realize that they are unlikely ever to lose their basic wildness. Their public relations with other pets were deplorable.

The remaining five species of Felidae found in Africa are all about the size of a house cat — indeed, two of them are among its most likely ancestors.

All have in common the fact that they have been remarkably little studied, though two are widespread and occur also in Asia.

THE AFRICAN WILDCAT (Plate 11)

Also known as the Egyptian cat and Kaffir cat, this animal has had many scientific names; *Felis libyca* now holds the field. It is found throughout the continent except in the great deserts and the equatorial rain forests. The wildcats of Crete, Sardinia, Corsica, and Majorca are regarded as geographical races of the same species, and its range extends into Asia. It is slightly larger and heavier than the house cat. The head and body are about two and one-quarter feet and its tail another one and one-quarter feet long. The average weight is about eight pounds. The general pattern resembles a tabby house cat of the Abyssinian type, the dark body stripes being rather thin. There are dark rings round the tail and upperparts of the limbs, the tail tip and legs usually being black. There are blackish streaks on the face and a spot in front of each eye. The underparts are much lighter, and females are generally paler than males, with less definite markings. The backs of the ears are rufous — a good point for identification.

The wildcat is typically nocturnal, though you may see it about on dull days. Its haunts are rather open forest country, where it lies up in cover or down a hole during the day, coming out at night to hunt small mammals and birds, especially game birds and domestic poultry, whenever it can get the chance. Its voice is like that of the house cat, but lower and harsher, according to C. T. A. Maberley.

African wildcats interbreed freely with house cats, and Stevenson-Hamilton had a first-generation male hybrid for five years. It disliked being handled and lived a part of its life in the wild, but was friendly with the station dogs and did not attack chickens. It was an adept snake hunter and ironically met its end in the jaws of a python.

THE JUNGLE CAT (Plate 22)

The jungle cat of India, *Felis chaus,* also inhabits Egypt, but very little seems to have been written about its life in this region. The head and body are two to two and one-half feet long, with the tail adding another ten inches. It stands about fifteen inches and may weigh as much as twenty pounds. The coat color varies from gray to tawny, with a weak tabby pattern superimposed, and the tail is black-ringed. There is a distinct crest of hair along the back, and the ears are slightly tufted. The underparts and the area round the mouth are almost white.

THE SAND CAT (Plate 11)

This beautiful little cat was first identified on the borders of Algeria and Tripolitania about one hundred years ago; a specimen was obtained on one of the expeditions led by General Margueritte, who did so much to open up the French Sahara — the specific name *margarita* is in his honor. The sand cat is rather smaller than the African wildcat and well adapted for desert life, being sandy fawn in color, with a few stripes on its legs and a black patch on the outer ears. The feet are covered by dense, rather coarse hairs which almost hide the pads and are obviously useful when gripping slippery sand. The big ears suggest acute hearing and they are widely separated, as in Pallas's cat (see p. 78), and presumably for the same reason of allowing it to peer over boulders — it lives in rocky wastes as well as sand desert — without being conspicuous. The fennec fox has similar adaptations and so has the jerboa, which is probably the principal prey of both, forming, together with them, a neat little desert community.

Specimens were taken at Aïr in 1925 and at El Golea (30° N) in 1931 and put in separate races; and there were at least two in Egyptian zoos before the First World War. Meanwhile a desert cat had been identified in what is now Turkmenia and called *Eremaelurus thinobius*. Specimens closely resembled the African ones; the difficulty was the wide gap in distribution. Could Arabia supply the missing link? In 1948 part of a skin reached the British Museum from Wilfred Thesiger, who got it from an Arab in the Empty Quarter. Finally in 1952 the London Zoo was presented with a live young sand cat, from about 150 miles north of the Aden Protectorate. It lived in captivity for eight years before its death through an accident and was often watched by R. W. Hayman, to whom I am indebted for these notes concerning it.

So the chain was complete. Though not all the authorities are satisfied, I am a lumper by nature and happy to agree with the distinguished Russian scientists who have made *Felis margarita* and *F. thinobius* one species. Very

little is known of its habits. It is probably nocturnal, lying up in shallow
holes during the day.

AFRICAN GOLDEN CAT (Plate 11)

The beautiful *Felis aurata* is confined to the tropical forests of Africa
and should not be confused — though anyone might be pardoned for doing
so — with the closely related Asian golden cat, *F. temmincki* (see p. 76). It
is about three feet in length of which ten inches is tail, and is remarkable
because it exists in two color phases, golden and gray, side by side. Sir Harry
Johnston said that the typical golden form is smaller and coppery red above;
the gray is larger but with shorter hair and a golden-yellow fringe between
upper- and underparts. The upperparts may be rather indistinctly spotted,
but the whitish underparts are clear. The tail is ringed and the ears are
rounded, with dark tips. Strict natural selection would suggest that each
color form confers certain advantages, so that both are enabled to survive
together in the same habitat. But such theorizing is upset by the undoubted
record of one that changed color when in the London Zoo.

The golden cat is reputed to be a merciless killer; it is apt to raid poultry
and is known as the "leopard's brother" to the tribes of the Liberian interior. It is now very rare in Kenya, and I have yet to see it alive in the wild.

THE BLACK-FOOTED CAT (Plate 11)

Last on the list is the black-footed cat of southern Africa, *Felis nigripes*.
It is also now rather rare and probably confined to the Kalahari Desert,
Bechuanaland, western districts of the Orange Free State, and parts of the
Transvaal and eastern Cape. It is a little smaller than a house cat, with a
rather pale tawny coat, becoming white underneath and on the inside of
the limbs. The body is marked with small spots that fuse into stripes on
neck and shoulders. Each leg has three dark rings and the rather stout tail
is black-tipped. The ears are slightly pointed; the soles of the feet are black,
hence the scientific and English names. Like its relations, it is nocturnal
and is believed to hunt birds, reptiles, and small mammals, lying up by
day in holes in the ground, where the kittens, in litters of two or three, are
also born. It has been crossed successfully with the house cat.

So much for the cats of Africa. It is obvious that our knowledge of their

Cats of Asia.   Plates 3, 4

above: Tiger eating
below: Jaguar in water
right: Jaguar, dark form

facing page 49 (Plate 4): Scottish wildcat

habits is directly proportional to their size. In the final chapter I shall review their chances of survival. It is clear already that we know next to nothing about the present status of the last three small species, which may all be in danger of extinction.

5. The Cats of Asia

THE VAST LAND MASS of Asia has been called the cradle of man. It also seems to be the crucible in which many other species of animal were forged before spreading out to colonize the rest of the Old World and, it is possible, the New World as well. Certainly, as far as the Felidae are concerned, Asia is the most important continent, the probable home of most of the Old World cats. Indeed, only the serval, the African golden cat, and the black-footed cat are not found in Asia, and the last two may quite well have evolved recently into distinct species from an ancestor shared with an Asian relative.

Unfortunately, though I have made many journeys in Asia since my early visit to Bali, I have not had the opportunities to study at first hand its cats that have come my way in Africa. This is partly because active conservation is less advanced in the East: there are few areas it is possible to visit with the same good hope of seeing the larger animals at home which one can entertain in the parks and game reserves of East, central, and South Africa. There are, of course, a number of important sanctuaries in India, and I am much indebted to E. P. Gee for the information he has put at my disposal about the Indian lion in particular; we must hope that the efforts of a few individuals like him will result in even more effective conservation of the wonderful fauna still left in the subcontinent.

THE TIGER (Plates 3, 12, 13, 14)

The tiger must take pride of place among Asia's cats, but it still awaits its Guggisberg. Studying the accounts of its natural history that are available, one comes across the same statements repeated from author to author with slight modifications and deriving from something written perhaps a century and more ago. This always happens when there is a lack of firsthand observation and shows, I am afraid, that very few good naturalists have yet studied this magnificent animal in the field except over the sights of a sporting rifle.

Man's relations with the tiger, in fact, have been almost entirely on a kill-or-be-killed basis, and that is not a good foundation for dispassionate study. But since one man-eater is credited with causing the destruction of thirteen villages and the desertion of more than 250 square miles of land — about half an average English county — one can see the practical reasons for a policy of extermination.

The tiger is generally believed to have originated in the north of Eurasia and to have spread southward. This theory is based on: the discovery of fossils in the extreme north of Siberia dating from Pleistocene times; its retention of a thick winter coat which is molted rapidly in central India in spring; its present distribution in Manchuria and Amur and at heights up to 8000 feet in the foothills of the Himalayas and the Altai; and its failure to reach Africa and Ceylon. Reginald I. Pocock suggested that it moved southwest and southeast on either side of the Tibetan plateau, probably entering India by way of Burma round the east end of the Himalayas. He based this view on the continuity of distribution and the resemblance between the local tiger populations along the route. Although failing to colonize Ceylon, presumably because it was already separated from India, tigers reached most of the islands of Southeast Asia. They were still to be found in Bali when I was there. There are fifty different local names for tiger in Malaysia and India, where there is archeological evidence of their presence five thousand years ago. The southwestern thrust brought tigers into Turkestan and Persia, where they still survive, but not into Asia Minor or Europe except in the mountains of Georgia.

The character and appearance of the tiger have been dictated to many of us by Rudyard Kipling's picture of the crafty, solitary, treacherous Shere Khan in the Jungle Books. As an antidote, here is an impression of one from Captain James Forsyth, lying in wait for it at dawn: "He looked such a picture of fearful beauty! — with his velvety step and undulating movements, the firm muscles working beneath his loose glossy skin, and the cruel yellow eyes blinking up at the sun over a row of ivory teeth, as he licked his lips and whiskers after a night's feed." His last licks, because these lyrical sentiments did not prevent the gallant captain from shooting the tiger forthwith!

Everyone has a general idea of what a tiger looks like, but it is perhaps more variable in size and color than any other big cat. Though Pocock considered there was no proved example of a black tiger, "white" specimens are well known, particularly from India. One, in which the striped pattern was only visible under reflected light, was exhibited in England early in the nineteenth century. Recently the Maharajah of Rewa distributed most of his famous collection and a young pair were sent to the Bristol Zoo, where we often visit our good friend R. E. Greed, the Director, combining it with a discussion of future television series at the B.B.C.'s Natural History Unit, based in the same city. These Rewa tigers have charcoal-colored stripes on a white ground, pink noses and pads, and ice-blue eyes. I suppose the form is more correctly described as an extreme "dilute" rather than as a true albino. In general, the tigers of Siberia and China are paler, with longer fur; and the populations become brighter as we go south to the smaller, dark tigers of Sumatra, which are buff-colored instead of white on the face. In all these races — for the splitters have enjoyed themselves with the tiger as with the lion — the stripes may vary on individual animals both in their number and density.

The skeleton, musculature, and general dimensions of the tiger resemble those of the lion. The combined head and body length of males ranges from five feet eight inches to seven feet three inches; tigresses are smaller, from just over five feet. The tail may be from two and one-half feet to three feet long, so that a really big male is about nine and one-half feet in total length; a ten-footer is exceptional. Longer measurements are probably of stretched skins. Tigers stand three feet or less at the shoulder, very seldom taller. The weight range is considerable. A. A. Dunbar Brander recorded Indian males from 353 to 512 pounds, with a mean of 420 pounds, but his tigresses averaged only 290 pounds. The heaviest tiger ever recorded is said to have scaled 645 pounds — far more than the heaviest lion; and in build it is a rather more massive animal, with a particularly powerful foreleg and paw, suggesting the stealthy pounce rather than the fleet pursuit.

As with measurements, so most of our information about the tiger's natural history comes from India, collected by sportsmen as a sideline to what they no doubt considered their more serious business with it, though we have Harry R. Caldwell's *Blue Tiger* about the animal in China in the first quarter of this century. It is not now found in desert country; its favorite haunts are dense thickets, long grass, or, in hot weather, tamarisk scrub along the riverbanks. Tigers rest in cover during the day and many years ago their fondness for ruins — the courts where Jamshid gloried and drank deep — was commented on: they will lie along the top of an old wall like a leopard on the bough of a tree. There seems some doubt about how well they can actually climb. Of a number of records of them attacking sportsmen in tree-hides, or machans, perhaps the most famous involved Mrs. E. A. Smythies, the wife of a forest officer. A wounded tiger put its forelegs round the tree on which her hide was built, and clawed its way up fourteen feet. When Mrs. Smythies saw its head appear over the edge, she thrust her rifle down its throat, pulled the trigger — and had a misfire. The tiger then forced one paw through the floor of the platform, so the lady stepped backward and fell over the side. Meanwhile her husband, from his machan, fired and killed the tiger, which also dropped to the ground. But as tigers are credited with leaps of twenty feet, not much climbing ability would be needed to carry them up to most machans, which are from ten to fifteen feet high. Their claw marks may be seen on favorite trees up to eight feet.

Tigers swim well and may visit islands in the big rivers to hunt, and in Malaya they have been seen swimming across bays for miles; they also cool off in water on very hot days. They may wander long distances, and have often been tracked for tens of miles. This roving along nullahs and game tracks is probably in search of game. The tiger on the prowl walks slowly, leaving parallel tracks, with the rear pugmark on each side just in advance of the front one. Though usually solitary, as depicted by Kipling, tigers may be found in parties of three or four, which are perhaps family groups — or groups brought together by chance to a spot rich in game.

The tiger's prey, like that of the other big cats, varies a good deal according to locality and opportunity. In southern India deer, especially the big sambar and less commonly the spotted deer, are killed, and wild pigs are a favorite in many areas. The Kirghis say tigers arrive when pigs are numerous. Caldwell says pangolins are taken, and their scales recovered by the Chinese because of their medicinal value. There is now a long tradition of cattle-killing by tigers. In some Indian districts they take a huge annual toll: it has been estimated that more than 30,000 head of cattle may be killed every year in the whole country. Occasionally a herd will face a tiger and drive him off, and there are even cases of wild boars re-taliating successfully and killing their arch-enemy. Adult buffaloes are formidable opponents; tigers normally only tackle young ones. On the other hand, there are records of tigers pulling down elephants, wounding them so badly that they died afterwards, but these incidents probably took place during hunts. At the other end of the scale, they are sometimes reduced to killing and eating lizards and frogs, and like lions and leopards in Africa they run into trouble from porcupine quills. Caldwell tells of a Chinese who was killed when carrying a sack of frogs; his body was not removed but the sack was ripped open. The tiger had presumably been attracted by the croaking. There are also records of tigers eating crocodiles, tortoises, and fish; even of one with a stomach full of locusts.

The tiger roars, though not so often as the lion, and also growls and snarls; it has a whoof of surprise and is credited with a belling call like that of the sambar stag, one of its principal prey — in fact, it has even been suggested that the tiger bells to attract the big deer! This noise, also described as "titting" or "pooking," has caused a great deal of controversy; it seems most likely to be a call of alarm. Another curious sound is the "moaning" uttered when a tiger is moving about in cover. Tigers, like other roaring cats, cannot purr, and Frederick W. Champion thinks the moaning sound is equivalent to the purring of smaller species and shows satisfaction.

The usual hunting method of the tiger is a slow stalk through cover, close enough for a final spring, when the strong forepaws knock the victim over and the tremendous jaws close on its neck to give the coup de grâce. Smaller animals are usually attacked from in front and gripped by the throat, larger ones at the nape, the paws coming round in a deadly hug that twists the neck — sometimes so the head faces backward — but does not necessarily break it. The biggest prey of all, such as the buffalo, may be hamstrung first from behind. This is said to be the regular method of Burmese tigers. Caldwell says Chinese tigers attack from the side and below, fastening their fangs in the victim's neck by the jugular vein and breaking it by a sudden wrench, their forepaws placed on the chest. He once saw a tiger land on the back of a water buffalo cow, who was with a calf. But she flinched and it skidded off into the mud, whence it picked itself up and stalked off defeated. Occasionally two tigers hunt and attack together, or one drives the prey to the other in ambush, as lions do. However, because of its nocturnal habits, human observers are seldom able to watch the tiger at work, though there are many stories of the maddened charge of a cornered animal. We are indeed fortunate in Africa that we can watch lions and cheetahs almost at our ease.

According to one estimate, the tiger may kill an animal the size of an ox every five days; this, of course, makes it a much heavier predator than the lion on the figures given on page 27. Young animals are supposed to be even more destructive, killing four or five beasts in one night just for the sake of killing. I am inclined to regard these high estimates with caution; they probably represent maximum kills and isolated incidents from which it is always tempting to generalize. Champion's more moderate figure was an average of fifty deer a year. There are also remarkable accounts of the tiger's ability to drag a cow over a high fence, and Caldwell records one carrying a heifer up a twelve-foot bank, while a big male dragged a hog weighing 200 pounds for half a mile. Like its relatives, the tiger has a distinctive feeding routine: it consumes the hindquarters on the night of the kill, then before resting hides the carcass until the next visit, when the remainder of the body up to the head is eaten; the bones are polished off at the third sitting. Tigers are extremely circumspect when returning to a kill and may circle round it first for some time. They will eat carrion occasionally, and cannibalism is on record. Sir Walter Elliot, a much quoted authority on the tigers of southern India in the nineteenth century, describes how after a tigress had been shot the male dragged the body away and ate part of it. Tigers also eat their own cubs, but probably not before they are already dead or dying from other causes. They are also said to be fond of durian fruit, which has a distinctly "high" flavor.

As with lions, man-eating is generally attributed to elderly animals which are not able to hunt more active game, though sometimes tigresses with young cubs take to it. About a century ago seems to have been the peak period of destruction in India — I have already mentioned the huge area which one man-eater caused to be deserted. In 1869 tigers killed 127 people in another district and stopped the use of a public road for weeks, while the number of deaths attributed to tigers in the Central Provinces from 1866 to 1896 was nearly a thousand. Caldwell mentions several daring attacks in China and says that sixty people were killed in one district in a few weeks.

Naturally a menace on this scale could not be tolerated, and tigers were continually hunted and killed by Europeans with their superior weapons. Even as early as 1825–1829 Thomas C. Jerdon reported that 1032 were killed in Khandesh district. So it says a lot for Shere Khan's evasive ability that his kin are as numerous and widely distributed as they are today.

Most people have heard of the massive ceremonial tiger hunts organized by rajahs and other potentates for visiting celebrities. Only the outbreak of war in 1939 saved me from attending one organized by the Maharajah of Nepal. At these hunts, the tiger is located by shikaris, or trackers, and then surrounded by elephants — some carrying sportsmen in their howdahs — until it is forced into the open, makes a despairing attack on an elephant, and falls riddled with bullets.

Such spectacles are only for great occasions, but elephant-back has long been recognized as one of the best places from which to shoot a tiger, and there are innumerable accounts of such hunts in the reminiscent literature of British India. Characteristic examples occur in the pages of *My Indian Journal* by Colonel Walter Campbell of Skipness, who went out as an officer in the army at the age of seventeen in 1830. His diary gives the factual basis for the adventures he described under the guise of fiction in *The Old Forest Ranger,* a second book. The tyro Charles is initiated into big-game hunting by the experienced Mansfield (perhaps a combination of the author's brother George and his cousin the redoubtable Walter Elliot), with the Scots Dr. MacPhie as comic relief, fair cousin Kate as somewhat belated feminine interest (her pompous father to see that the course of true love shall not run too smoothly), and numerous faithful but expendable Indian retainers.

Early in 1831 Campbell was on leave with Elliot at Dharwar in the Bombay Presidency and records: "We have opened our campaign gloriously! Yesterday I shot two spotted bucks before breakfast; and to-day we have taken the scalp of the famous wandering tiger, which has been the terror of the neighborhood for the last six months."

Borrowing the elephant Anak from a friendly rajah, the party found that the tiger had been marked into "a small open ravine . . . every rising ground within sight was crowned by a look-out man, to turn him or mark him down if he should break away." The sportsmen mounted Anak and the tiger was bolted by a rattle of tomtoms and shouts; he was away with a loud roar "at a loping gallop." He passed the elephant 150 yards off but a long shot hit him and he disappeared over the hill. He was marked down again and the beaters were called on, all but one man who "intoxicated with opium, ignored every signal," drew his sword, and waved it defiantly at the approaching tiger. Anak could not get to the spot in time, and "one savage roar rang through the soul of the stricken wretch" before the tiger had him "writhing like a crushed worm in his grip." When the elephant was within range, six barrels sent the killer staggering back, but "he rallied instantly and made a brilliant charge close up to the elephant's trunk" only to be blown back by another volley from the spare guns. The party reloaded and gave him "shot after shot" until he fell. "He was game to the last and Elliot, who has killed many tigers, says he never saw one die more gallantly."

I have quoted this hunt because it has all the typical colorful ingredients of a hunting story of the period, even to a detailed description of the agony of the dying beater, which I spare the reader. The tiger when skinned was found to have stopped sixteen balls, "a strong proof of the extraordinary tenacity of life possessed by these animals." One could say the same for the author too, for within a few months, though still a boy, he weathered an attack of cholera which decimated his regiment. He also survived a face-to-face encounter "within twenty yards of a royal tiger, busily engaged in tearing up the carcass of a wild hog he had just killed." He was saved by the presence of mind of his Indian guide who fixed his eyes on the tiger until, "as if appalled by the steady gaze of the savage," it slunk away. His savior was a remarkable young man who had shot a tiger when fifteen and had been beaten by his father for it, because, as a jungle dweller, he considered it wise to be on good terms with the *bagh*.

But the father's attitude was not typical. Bussapa, the best tiger hunter of the southern Mahratta country, regarded the "whole feline race" with mortal hatred and once spent a night within three yards of a wounded tiger without its noticing him — an incident strongly vouched for and throwing a curious light on the animal's sense of smell, which most authorities believe to be deficient. Campbell also records a fight between a tiger and a bear, but they were two of a number of large animals enclosed by a ring of beaters and the behavior was probably abnormal: the sort of "confrontation" of which some modern film-makers still dream, but which if seen on the screen can only have been brought about artificially.

As an alternative to the elephants, elevated tree-hides are widely used. The tiger is either driven toward the machan or lured to the spot by a decoy animal at night. Nowadays, the use of live decoys is prohibited in India but dead animals are used by photographers as well as by shooters.

A most unusual method of hunting a tiger was practiced by the Indians in the Wynaad. They surrounded it and drove it into a large net in which it could be speared in comparative safety. In *The Old Forest Ranger* Mansfield and Charles try this method with almost disastrous results: the tiger nearly breaks through, but Dr. MacPhie comes to the rescue with Mons Meg, his trusty weapon. Netting, of course, is still used to capture tigers alive. But the most remarkable and potentially suicidal of all tactics must be that attributed to the Manchu Tartars, who dug a pit with a raised island on which a warrior stood. The pit was then covered over and when a tiger obligingly fell in the hidden hero stabbed him! In China a cage of stout bamboos was used instead of a pit, with a kid as bait, and the intrepid hunter crouched alongside. When a tiger jumped on the cage, he stabbed it through the bars. Spring-guns, traps, pits, and poison have all been used in India by villagers, who in some areas formed tiger clubs, pledged to destroy each animal as it entered the district.

By way of contrast to these feats I should like to come almost up to date, to the days of Elephant Bill, the late Colonel J. H. Williams, who tells the tale of Willie's first tiger. Willie, a newcomer to Burma, was invited to a jungle-fowl shoot but had no gun. He was lent a rifle of small caliber and told to pot ground game after it had passed the line of other guns. But at the end of the third drive his neighbors "were horrified to see that he had disobeyed instructions and fired in front of him, towards the beaters. 'What the hell do you think you are doing, young man?' demanded 'Growler' Moore, going up to him in a fury. 'What on earth are you firing at?' 'I saw a tiger,' said Willie. 'Tiger? What d'you mean, tiger? Don't talk nonsense!' shouted Growler. . . . 'Well, there it is, and it's dead,' said Willie." And so it was, with a bullet through its head — a far cry from Walter Campbell's sixteen balls, and a fitting end to this look at tiger hunting. However we may laugh at these bygone sportsmen or deplore the inroads they made on the wildlife of India, there can be no denying their courage and an indifference to hardships which the airborne, car-borne naturalist of today has almost forgotten.

The pioneer of photography rather than the rifle in India is Frederick W. Champion, who, beginning in the 1920's, made a number of successful daylight and flashlight exposures of tigers and other jungle animals, sometimes using a trip wire so that the subject took its own picture. The photoelectric cell technique had not yet appeared. Later he started filming in black and white and color with considerable success. Usually he worked from an elephant or a hide, spending many dew-soaked nights in the forest. His entertaining books *With a Camera in Tiger-Land* and *The Jungle in Sunlight and Shadow* recount failures as well as triumphs with delightful candor and add a good deal to our knowledge of the tiger's habits. He several times met one at close quarters. Once his party found one watching them from a few feet away, and another investigated all his apparatus, fortunately in his absence. I am very glad to be able to reproduce some of his outstanding studies in this book.

Harry R. Caldwell also remarks on the tiger's patience; one waited for three hours in full view of a goat bait for the coast to be clear. If not satisfied as to safe conditions, it may quietly disappear. At other times it will attack boldly, even when animals are being led on a rope.

Tigers in the wild resemble lions in breeding only when the cubs of the previous litter are able to look after themselves, at between two and three years of age. They are born in thick cover — for example, the "null" grass of India — and the litter size is from one to four, occasionally up to six. But it is unusual for more than two to survive. In captivity, thirty litters averaged 1·53 according to Brand, who quotes a gestation period of 105 to 109 days and says that zoo tigers, like their relatives, show no special breeding season. The cubs are striped at birth, weigh under three pounds, and open their eyes in fifteen to sixteen days. The natural life span of the tiger is about twenty years, as with the lion, but few wild tigers reach this venerable age.

If our knowledge of the tiger's natural history is still a bit scanty, we have no lack of superstitions and legends. Many old writers describe how, as soon as the beast was killed, their shikari would singe off its whiskers to prevent its spirit haunting him or, on other accounts, because they contained a deadly poison. Yet in parts of southern India, according to Jerdon, they were considered to be a powerful aphrodisiac — perhaps only the other side of the same coin. It was also believed that the tiger added a lobe to its liver for every year of its life, that its flesh possessed medicinal virtues, and that a necklet of its claws would protect a child from the evil eye. In Korea tiger skins were worn by the chiefs, no doubt in the hope that they would confer the animal's nobler qualities on the wearer.

More sinister is the concept of a ghost tiger, *Nat kyah,* which Elephant Bill encountered in Burma. One of his men, a notorious atheist, disappeared from his hut in the night. There were "the indisputable pugmarks and tracks of a tiger that had sprung up into the hut and down again" and signs of a body being dragged down to the shallow creek nearby. But there the tracks ended, and no one could pick them up again. It is just conceivable that the man was murdered because of his blasphemies and perfect evidence of a tiger's visit was provided, in which case I am reminded of the "lion men" who terrorized parts of Kenya recently, and of the "leopard men" of the old Congo.

Tigers are almost as famous as zoo and circus animals as lions and must have as long a history of captivity. In Chapter 3 I mentioned hybrids between them. Captive tigers have the reputation of being more cowardly and treacherous than lions, but I think this is largely due to the preconceived notions of their "characters," to which I referred in the first chapter.

We have already met the next three big cats of Asia in Africa, but whereas the leopard — often known as the panther in India — has shown on both continents the same capacity for weathering human persecution, the state of both lion and cheetah in Asia is very much worse.

THE INDIAN LION (Plates 15, 16)

The lion was once widespread, extending through Asia Minor into Europe, but its preference for open country, compared with the thicker cover favored by tiger and leopard, was probably its undoing; it also occurred in the mountains up to 5000 feet in Persia, where there have been odd records in quite recent years.

During the early days of British rule in India, lions were still locally common, but they were no match for the sporting officers, one of whom killed 300, fifty of them near Delhi in the decade 1850–1860. Another, who enjoyed chasing and shooting them from horseback, accounted for eighty in three years. When Jerdon wrote, about a century ago, they were confined to the northwest and were only common in Gujarat and Kutch. Little was known of their habits; they were said to prey on bullocks and donkeys, and their fat was prized as a cure for rheumatism. By 1880 their range was reduced to about two thousand square miles in the Kathiawar peninsula.

Even with their relatively poor manes, lions were preferred to lionesses as trophies and this led to an unbalanced sex ratio, which E. P. Gee believes further contributed to their decline; tigers and tigresses, of course, were shot impartially. But, bearing in mind the promiscuous behavior of African lions, I should have thought that the difference in numbers would have to be considerable before it could affect breeding adversely.

The dimensions of the Indian lion, which we may for once agree with the splitters is a justifiable distinct subspecies, are much the same as for the African race: total length varies from eight and one-half to nine and one-half feet, the height at shoulder is about three and one-half feet and the weight of a good male is about 500 pounds. Mr. Gee, who has seen many Indian lions in the field at close quarters, says they are stockier and sturdier than their cousins, a view which I think his photographs support. Young and immature animals are less spotted and become shaggier when adult, with a bigger tail-tuft. They are not so white on the belly, but paler on head and neck. He considers the comparative lack of mane — it is never actually absent, in spite of the nickname "camel-tiger" — is an adaptation to the lower altitudes, only 200 to 400 feet above the sea, at which the present remnant lives.

The "maneless lion of Gujarat" owed its survival to the rulers of Junagadh. At one time, at the beginning of the century, it was given out that only a dozen were left, and Lord Curzon graciously forwent the honor of shooting one; but it is probable that there were really about a hundred in the 500 square miles of Gir Forest, which is now a reserve and remains their stronghold.

Gee describes the habitat as a dry, hilly area of rather open and thin deciduous forest, mainly of undersized teak. There is usually about forty inches of rain from July to September, but by November the grass is dried up and the lions match it perfectly. In January flame-of-the-forest makes brilliant color to delight the photographer. The other larger inhabitants of the sanctuary include sambar, spotted deer, blue buck, nilgai, chinkara, wild pig, and peafowl, but the main food of the lions is village buffaloes and cattle. This leads to guerrilla warfare and a curious artificial balance of nature: just enough lions seem to be killed, mostly by poison, to prevent overpopulation. But numbers have climbed slowly. Censuses based on measured pugmarks — which are as individual as fingerprints — are fairly easy to take, because the lions like walking along the forest roads. In 1950 the figure was 219 to 227, in 1955 it was 250, in 1958 290, and this is about where it stands as I write.

The Gir lions have become quite a tourist attraction. Keshod airport is only one and one-half hours by air from Bombay and a forty-mile drive takes the visitor to the comfortable resthouse at Sasan Gir. Here lion shows are arranged by the shikaris, who put out kills in suitable places. Spectators are screened behind branches and a live goat is used as the dinner bell, and removed before the "guests" arrive. Gee says the Gir lions are "reasonably well-behaved": one male came within ten feet of his flimsy hide after sniffing at a family of cubs, and at one moment he had in view lionesses with three and four cubs and a pregnant one, as well as the head of the pride. The lions can also be seen by car headlights at night, but this does not compare with daylight observations at a "kill."

Perhaps the Indian lion has an old reputation for relative harmlessness, because Walter Campbell recounts what a friend told him about a lion hunt in Gujarat. "I was infinitely diverted with one of the village coolies who accompanied us, his matchlock over his shoulder, the pan carefully closed with a bit of cloth, and a lump of burning cow-dung in his hand, with which to ignite his match if necessary. This worthy, thus equipped, was literally poking his addled head into the very centre of the bush, said to contain the lion, and, moreover, pulling the grass aside to admit of a better view. 'What, in the name of Heaven, are you doing?' exclaimed my companion. 'Doing!' replied the fellow, with evident surprise, and coolly blowing his fid of cow-dung. 'Why, looking for the lion, to be sure! Are you not looking for him?'"

It is sometimes suggested that since the lion was probably in India long before the tiger, it has suffered in competition with the reputedly more powerful animal. Gee believes that their different choice of habitat would keep them from serious contact. There are no accepted accounts of their meeting and fighting in the wild, but artificial duels have been arranged; the known result, to imitate the football scores, is Lions 4, Tigers 3.

There have been several attempts to reinforce or extend the range of the Indian lion. The ruler of Gwalior introduced some African lions to Shivpuri about 1916 but they were soon killed off; a supposed importation about 1880 specially for a shoot by the Duke of Clarence seems to have no basis in fact. But in 1957 a lion and two lionesses from the Gir Forest were moved to Chandraprabha sanctuary in Uttar Pradesh, where they have bred and increased slightly. Since the lion and not the tiger is the emblem of India, we must hope that national prestige, as well as good conservation, will not only save this fine race but encourage its spread into suitable reserved areas of its former range.

THE LEOPARD (Plate 17)

Under one of his chapter titles Frederick Champion quotes from A. I. R. Glassfurd: "The tiger is, as a rule, a gentleman. The panther, on the other hand, is a bounder." For a long time there was confusion about the number of kinds of bounder to be found in Asia, because the leopard, or panther as it is usually called in India, seemed to come in quite different sizes and colors. I must own I find it all confusing myself. One writer speaks of larger, paler animals in the hills, another of forest animals being bigger than those in hill country. Theodore Roosevelt said he could detect no difference between the leopard skins from the Sudan and Java, the one well to the west, the other about as far east as leopards go. Perhaps we can agree that forest populations, following a fairly general rule, are darker than those inhabiting open country, but size is probably very much a matter of individual variation. The black panther — Kipling's Bagheera, and surely not a bounder! — was once regarded as a distinct species but is now known simply as a mutation, fairly common in parts of India. In extreme examples, the black coat appears uniform, the spot pattern being visible only in very bright light, and the tint even extends to the tongue, gums and palate; the eyes may be blue, enhancing an already remarkable animal. Another striking variety seems to have yellow spots on a black ground, so closely are they concentrated. Since black animals continue to appear, it seems they are at no great disadvantage against their normal kin at making a living in the jungle. Albinistic panthers are as rare as melanistic tigers.

Since the leopard is the most widespread of the big cats, it would not be surprising to find several geographical races that showed reasonably constant characters; but I hesitate to accept the eleven forms once described for Asia. The modern range extends from near the Mediterranean coast in Syria, through Iran northward to Manchuria and Korea; over much of China and most of India to Burma, the Malay Peninsula and Java, and — unlike the tiger — to Ceylon. It even claims a tiny European foothold in Kuban, north of the Caucasus, relict of a Pleistocene distribution as far as Spain.

In general the African leopard does not change its spots or its habits by becoming an Asian panther, but a few years ago two members of the staff of the Wild Life Department in Ceylon made some excellent firsthand observations on its hunting methods, of a kind so rare where the big cats of Asia are concerned that I think they will bear quotation in some detail.

One evening W. L. A. Andris came upon a leopard lying beneath a tree. He retired to watch. The leopard in its turn was watching a herd of spotted deer grazing about a hundred yards away and moving slowly toward it. It lay on its belly, forelegs stretched, motionless except for periodically tossing its tail. These "nervous" tail movements are characteristic of the whole family, from the tiger to the house cat, and indicate intense concentration, often leading to violent action.

As the deer came closer, the leopard gradually drew in its forelegs, keeping its head low. When they were only twenty yards away, it sprang at a doe, seizing her from the front with both paws round the neck and gripping the throat in its jaws. The other deer ran back some yards before stopping to bark and stamp. The doe stood for some minutes before falling over sideways; and the leopard pressed her downward until all struggles ceased. Then it released its grip, retired a few yards, sat down, and looked at its kill. Two or three times it sprang onto the doe, bit the neck, and sat down again. Finally it gripped the body by the neck, and dragged it, parallel to its own body, toward a pond. The rest of the herd followed at a distance, uttering their shrill alarm call.

Andris' second observation, also in the evening, involved a sounder of eight adult and seven suckling wild pigs, feeding in a muddy pool. A leopard came out of the jungle, sat down about 150 yards from the pigs, and watched them for twenty minutes before beginning a stalk that took it about half the distance. Then it lay flat, as observed before, still except for the twitching tail, while the unsuspecting pigs approached to within ten yards. Again there was a lightning spring and the leopard emerged from the sounder on three legs, one suckling "hooked in the claws of its right front paw," another in its mouth. It ran some seventy-five yards and climbed a malittan tree; the pigs pursued it, grunting and screaming, while the piglet held in its paw squealed; the other appeared to be dead. The pigs ran round under the tree and some rose on their hind legs, biting the bark. When the commotion ceased, Andris approached the tree and the pigs ran away. The leopard had killed both sucklings, placed one in a fork, and was eating the other.

The third observation, by A. Malhamy, took place at 7 A.M. during a drought. A leopard was walking 150 yards off across the dry bed of a pond. He followed it cautiously until it climbed a dan tree and lay along a bough about ten feet up, quite still, except for looking around from time to time. The tree was in fruit, and every day deer and pigs came to feed on the fallen berries. After half an hour, nine spotted deer approached the tree and the leopard became tense. A doe walked right under its hiding place; it sprang onto her back and bit into her throat. She cried out and, as Andris reported, the herd ran away before demonstrating. The doe fell over and the leopard continued to bite and claw her, tossing its tail from side to side. When she was still, the leopard walked away and sat down, panting. Then it got up and walked twice round the kill before seizing the dead doe by the neck and dragging her backward about twenty yards into the jungle and out of view.

It is interesting that the leopard evidently paid more respect to wild pigs than to deer after making a kill, and that individual animals behaved slightly differently. The general methods — stalking and ambush — are those I described in the preceding chapter. If only we had more of such excellent field notes, instead of obituary notices!

Spotted deer are a favorite prey of leopards in India too, whereas tigers prefer the larger sambar, an illustration of the ecological principle that each animal is primarily adapted to certain foods, though, of course, a leopard may easily take young or weak sambar and a tiger may kill spotted deer. Champion estimated that about forty leopards inhabited 300 square miles of reserved forest in the Himalayan foothills and, at an average of one kill a fortnight, consumed about one thousand spotted deer a year, including many pregnant does.

Leopards also hunt monkeys and smaller animals and this brings them into competition with lesser relatives, the clouded leopard and golden cat, also nocturnal tree-climbers. Many leopards take to living on domestic stock and become "village panthers." They will kill the whole range of hoofed animals, but dogs are their special weakness and incite them to feats of astonishing daring. A leopard sprang out of the jungle and snapped up a dog trotting just ahead of Walter Campbell's regiment on the march and vanished with it into the jungle on the other side of the road. Another took a bulldog that was chained to its master's bed! Sometimes all the dogs at a station have been spirited away; but no one has really explained their fascination for the leopard. On the other hand, mastiffs with spiked collars have been used to hunt their foe and occasionally have killed him themselves.

From the dog it is not a far cry to his master, and it seems agreed in Asia as in Africa that a man-killing leopard is worse than either a lion or a tiger. In 1858 one killed nearly one hundred people in Seoni, but the grim record belongs to the man-eater of Rudraprayag in Garhwal which, spreading its depredations over nine years, killed 125 people before the famous Jim Corbett shot it at night on May 1, 1926, as it came to a goat bait. It had taken months of effort, hampered by superstitious unwillingness on the part of the villagers to give information about it, because they believed they would be haunted by its spirit. This is probably similar to the feeling that makes people in Burma call a tiger *saya,* the master, when talking about it in the jungle.

One man who might have given us a sympathetic insight into the "bounder" of the big cats was EHA (Edward Hamilton Aitken), the Indian-educated Scot whose observant, humorous books are still prized by naturalists. Unfortunately, he passed most of his service in the prosaic Customs and Salt Department in arid localities near Bombay where leopards were scarce. But, as we would say today, he took the mickey out of big-game shooting in his story of "A Panther Hunt." He begins factually enough. The author and his colleague H. are taking a stroll after work near an old fort, "where the natives say there is generally a small panther." Sure enough, they hear a distinct sound like the sawing of wood, and soon see an object "like the head and ears of a large cat." It moves. " 'By the Accountant-General,' cried H., 'it *is* a panther. What shall we do? It will be down on the dogs.' " H. takes the dogs home while EHA throws a stone at the panther, which springs to its feet and jumps into the fort ditch. Next day the two men return armed and with their shikaris, and the tale begins to leave the ground. The shikaris are described in splendid parody of Walter Campbell and his like. Banawat Beg is "fair-skinned, small and spare, but supple as a cat. He was dressed in a suit of plain *khakee,* and wore on his head a small cap with flaps to pull over his ears when the wind blew cold," while Tajoob Khan carries a hunting knife with which he saved his master's life from a tiger, "Burying it to the hilt in the brute's heart." Tom-toms are not available, but the resourceful Banawat Beg hires a hundred kettles and large "handies," which make an abominable din when struck with hollow bamboos. Our heroes climb trees and the beat begins.

A large animal bolts, but as it passes a gap "not more than three inches wide," EHA shoots it through the heart; it is only a hyena. Then a jungle cat is "stopped with a bullet through the head." When the panther is finally dislodged by a Chinese cracker, it bowls the whole party over. They pursue it, firing recklessly. Tajoob Khan remonstrates with H., who knocks him down and then, lost to reason, advances on the now cornered panther. The panther springs, H. makes for a tree and sticks in a fork, where it has him at its mercy and soon "shreds of cloth and long strips of skin and flesh floated promiscuously upon the wind, which now began to howl through the branches of the trees." EHA hits the leopard on the head with a kettle — he has run out of shot — and finally kills it by firing a penknife from his rifle through its eye. The remains of H. are collected in a coolie's basket, but the measurement of the panther "was worthless, as poor H. had cut off nearly the whole of its tail with his first shot."

It must have taken courage for a mere excise officer to publish such a story in 1894. I hope my recounting it may revive interest in the gifted author of *A Naturalist on the Prowl,* even if he has no more to tell us about the cat family.

THE CHEETAH (African form shown on Plates 1, 2, 8)

The history of the cheetah in Asia is one of decline and no recovery. When the Bombay Natural History Society reviewed the status of the "wild animals of the Indian Empire" in 1935, it was all but extinct. According to Reginald I. Pocock, it was, like the tiger, an invader, entering India by way of Persia and Baluchistan and never extending farther south than the Deccan. Thus its range was much the same as that of the black buck, a favorite prey — another example of the close relation between a predator and its food animal. The latest dated record given by the Society is 1919 from the United Provinces, but rumors of its existence in the Central Provinces and elsewhere persisted. They were evidently correct, because three were shot in one night and a pair subsequently seen in Hyderabad as recently as 1951.

Elsewhere in Asia a remnant hangs on in Iran, perhaps also in Saudi Arabia and Oman. A female and cubs were taken in Iraq in 1928 but local Arabs did not know the animal. It is also just possible that some survive in Asian Russia.

A century ago, when Jerdon wrote, the cheetah was still widely distributed in India, in open country where it hunted the "common antelope," gazelle, nilgai, and occasionally sheep. But even then people were more familiar with its behavior in captivity. A young one brought up with greyhound puppies reminded me very much of our own Cheetah in Nairobi: it recognized its name and followed its master on horseback like a dog; it was fond of notice and purred like a cat. It attacked sheep until whipped, and donkeys until kicked; it could catch Bennett's gazelles but not pull them down; it appears that the hunting leopard has to be taught by its parents. The speed but not the skill is inherited.

Probably the best cheetahs were those caught as adults and tamed. This took about six months, the final stage being to accustom them to the human voice. They were sometimes caught in snares hung over the special trees to which they came to sharpen their claws, a habit shared with most if not all other cats.

Trained cheetahs were usually carried hooded in a cart. When game was seen, the hood was slipped, as is done with falcons, and the cheetah sprang down, sometimes on the opposite side of the cart, and set off in pursuit at a "surpassing velocity" up to about four hundred yards. This method seems to cut out the preliminary stalk, which was known to the Duke of Wellington when, as Sir Arthur Wellesley, he kept five cheetahs, once the property of Tippoo Sahib at Seringapatam. Sometimes the cheetah started walking toward unsuspecting game, gradually increasing speed into the final spring and running down. Bounding or springing at game was considered a bad habit. If its rush failed, the cheetah might walk on for several minutes "in a towering passion," before being helped back to its cart.

Cheetahs were trained to single out the best bucks in a herd, and if the run and kill were successful, were rewarded by a drink of the victim's blood before being hooded again.

Panther (from the Greek, and meaning "all animals") and leopard were originally names for the cheetah, which was thought to be a hybrid between a lion and a pard (what we now call a leopard). "Bearded as the pard" would be more applicable to the ruffed cheetah than to the true leopard. Still, poets cannot always be naturalists. We know that the sporting use of the cheetah goes back a very long time and reached Europe by way of Constantinople, whose Emperor Anastasius received a present of two A.D. 439. The sport spread to Italy and became popular among the princes of the Renaissance period. How long it has flourished in Arabia and North Africa we do not know. Attempts have been made to introduce cheetah racing in recent years both in Britain and America, but it has never become more than a curiosity. First the cheetahs caught and tore up the electric hare, and then refused to chase it when set at a speed too fast for them. They were too polite to race each other, but when pitted against greyhounds they easily caught them up and leaped gracefully over them.

THE SNOW LEOPARD (Plates 18, 19)

Panthera uncia is also called the ounce. This is one of the big-five roaring cats, the others being the lion, tiger, leopard, and jaguar. This classification is based on its anatomy, for there seems to be no record of anyone hearing its roar. Because of its short muzzle and other slight peculiarities of its skull it is sometimes placed in a special genus of its own. Externally, it is a most beautiful animal, a soft gray above, shading to white on the belly. The solid spots of the head and lower limbs become rosettes on the body and tail, and there is a black streak along the back. The tail is long, with heavy fur, and a thick body pelage is acquired in winter. The ears are black-edged with a white spot behind. The combined length of head and body is from three feet three inches to three feet eight inches, and the tail is from two feet nine inches to three feet; the shoulder height is about two feet.

Essentially adapted for mountain life, the snow leopard has its stronghold in the great massifs of central Asia: the Altai, Hindu Kush, and Himalaya; in the Himalaya it ranges from 6000 feet to 18,000 feet according to the season, and though it is said not to be particularly shy it is seldom seen by European observers; one recorded twelve sightings in more than twenty years. Stanley Jeeves, who was one of my cameramen on the expedition to look for the Abominable Snowman, saw one in the distance, "a blue-gray shadow against the stony hillside"; this was at 14,000 feet in the Chola Khola valley, close under Everest. It also occurs or has occurred northward into China. Supposed records from Asia Minor by British sportsmen refer to the pale leopards found in the hill areas there.

The haunts of the snow leopard are from the birch, pine, and scrub zone in winter, over the grassland to the snowline. It is nocturnal and feeds on the wild sheep "burhel" (*Pseudois nayaur*), ibex, musk deer, marmots, and other rodents. It may also attack sheep, goats, and dogs. One stayed near a flock of sheep all night even though pelted with stones. It has not been known to attack man. Most specimens have been shot or trapped in winter at lower altitudes. I can find no information about its breeding in the wild; in zoos two young have been born in a litter.

THE CLOUDED LEOPARD (Plate 20)

The clouded leopard (*Felis nebulosa*) is the largest Asian member of the purring cats, those with continuous hyoid bones. Large males may be three and one-half feet from head to tail base, with a three-foot tail; females are smaller, the total length five feet to five and one-half feet. Males from the Darjeeling area weighed thirty-nine pounds to forty-nine pounds and stood about twenty-one inches at the shoulder. A female from Sarawak weighed thirty-seven pounds.

The coat is variable in color, as with most cats, from gray or dark brown to a yellowish tint, becoming almost white on the belly. The head and face are strongly marked with darker streaks and spots, and it has been suggested that the pattern of the forehead may have a mesmeric effect. Two broad bands, with narrower bands between, run down the back, and the clouded appearance of the flanks is due to large blotches partly etched in dark brown and surrounded by pale spaces. There are spots and blotches on legs and belly, and dark rings round the bushy tail. The backs of the ears are black, with a buff spot on each. The body fur is short and rather coarse. The upper canine teeth are relatively more developed than in any other living cat, suggesting the famous saber-toothed tiger; in Sarawak they are used by certain tribes as ornaments in the ears.

The clouded leopard is essentially an Eastern species, found in Sikkim, Bhutan and Assam, Burma, Siam, the Malay Peninsula, Borneo, Sumatra, Formosa, and parts of mainland China. It is usually described as a tree-living cat of dense forests, sleeping or lying in ambush on branches and in forks, its main prey being birds and small mammals, though in Sumatra it lurks near villages to take chickens and sometimes larger animals. D. D. Davis says it will follow buffaloes with calves. E. M. Selous and E. Banks, who kept a young male for some time in Sarawak, give a rather different account of its habits, believing it to be more diurnal and terrestrial and an inhabitant of secondary woodland. Their pet was often active by day and was poor at balancing on branches. Also, when hunting wild pig with dogs, they twice brought to bay a wild clouded leopard on the ground. They say it is not a serious predator on livestock and that wild pig is its favorite prey; it will return to a kill repeatedly. They also found two kittens about five or six weeks old on the ground in the jungle. However, nothing seems to be known of the clouded leopard's breeding habits in the wild.

They are easily tamed if taken young. Banks and Selous consider them rather sluggish and less aggressive than the marbled cat. But their young male would not take dead meat and was fed on monkeys, chickens, and rats, attacking with a sudden rush and a quick blow from either of the very broad, rounded forepaws to knock them over or paralyze them. A single bite usually killed them. It ate two chickens a day, plucking them laboriously; a pigtailed monkey was tackled from the hind end, the fur being first removed by rasping with the tongue. The stance is normally slouching. On the move the head is kept low, the back straight, and the long tail, of which great care is taken, is curled sideways. Selous and Banks speak of an upright walk, a "slinking gait," a doglike trot, and a gallop. They describe the call as a "moaning roar," like wind over the mouth of an empty jar, a frightening sound at night when it is probably uttered from a chosen spot, one of the "tiger hills" that are well known in Borneo. The tame male also gave a peculiar chuckle when pleased or excited and a growl when annoyed. It was a placid animal and was frightened of the Flit pump used to spray its home.

On the other hand there are accounts of clouded leopards attacking men in Borneo. A pair dragged a male proboscis monkey from a low tree and killed it. The female then turned to attack a party of men who had been watching. They retired to their boat and shot her; but when they landed again to pick up the body the male went for them; and D. D. Davis records another attack by a female on a Malay. A Darjeeling male was picked up dead after an all-night fight with another cat or leopard.

THE MARBLED CAT (Plate 20)

A smaller edition of the clouded leopard is the usual description of the little-known marbled cat, another Eastern species found from the Himalayas to Java, Sumatra, and Borneo. Head and body total a little more than two feet and the tail is almost as long; the fur is soft and long and the marbled markings (from which derives its scientific name, *Felis marmorata*) are very variable. E. Banks says it inhabits clearings in the jungle and riverbanks, hunting largely on the ground and by night. It is reputed to be the "fiercest of all cats," striking and pinning down prey with its claws, then seizing them in its jaws. Its stance is characteristic: legs straight, back high-arched, tail in one complete curl. A captive marbled cat took squirrels, birds, and frogs but not carrion; the stomach of one shot at night in cut-over forest in North Borneo contained remains of some kind of rat. Banks says it utters "a low growl," in keeping with its temperament.

THE BORNEAN RED CAT (Plate 23)

Even less is known about two more small cats of Southeast Asia. The Bornean red cat (*Felis badia*) occurs also in Sarawak, where it was taken by A. C. Wallace in 1856. Its head and body make about twenty inches, its tail about fourteen inches. It is bright chestnut above, paler on the belly, and the ears are blackish brown. There is a white streak on the underside of the tail. Tom Harrisson, famous naturalist and anthropologist, is one of the few people who knows this animal. He considers it the most vicious of the family. He and a friend actually caught one when it was trying to swim a river and took a few feet of film, which has been shown on television; but no still photographs exist. It haunts great areas of rocky limestone on the edge of the jungle, up to 3000 feet, and Mr. Harrisson believes that it eats offal as well as small mammals and birds.

THE FLAT-HEADED CAT (Plate 23)

Also called the little Malayan red cat (*Felis planiceps*), this species has a body length, with the head, of twelve to twenty inches and a tail of six to eight inches. The weight range is three pounds twelve ounces to five pounds ten ounces, so it is one of the smaller members of the family in Asia. The coat is dark reddish brown above, with white tips to the hairs; the underparts from throat to belly are white, though with some spots; the tear-streaks are white, giving the face an unusual appearance.

It is found in Borneo, Sumatra, and Malaya, where it is very rare, according to Lim Boo Liat and Inche Abdul Rahmin bin Omar, who kept a young male from Selangor for a year. They only knew of two reports in fourteen years. Their captive, which was very tame, fed at first on milk, eggs, and dried prawns but rejected rice; later it would carry fish from a corner of the room into its cage to eat them. Its fur changed from gray to light brown and then to the glossy adult coat. It more than doubled its weight in a year to four and one-half pounds at its death.

Writing of it in Borneo, E. Banks described the flat-headed cat as nocturnal and hunting the riverbanks, where it takes frogs and fish. It has been caught in fish-traps. He says it does not take poultry but B. E. Smythies, Conservator of Forests in Sarawak and son of the heroine of the tiger story on page 53, saw one that was shot raiding chickens at night at the home of a Dayak headman. This is his only experience of the animal in some twenty years. Nothing is known of its breeding, except that Banks records a young one in January.

THE CHINESE DESERT CAT (Plate 23)

The Chinese desert cat (*Felis bieti*) was first described from two skins brought back to France by Prince Henri d'Orleans from the province of

Szechwan toward the end of the last century. Pocock believed it might be an intermediate species between the African wildcat and the sand cat, which occurs in Asia and is described on page 47. It is about the size of a house cat, and the coat is usually uniform, lacking any clear stripes or spots. The upperparts are yellowish gray with dark guard hairs, which give a darker appearance to the flanks. The throat is yellowish brown, the rest of the underparts white. There are indistinct markings on the face and legs. The base of the ears, which are about two inches long, is a pale reddish brown and there are three or four dark rings toward the tip of the tail, which is black and from nine to fourteen inches long. The head and body combined are from twenty inches to nearly three feet, but these measurements (probably a female) are from trade skins and may exaggerate the size of the live animal.

We know very little of the desert cat's habits. It seems to live on the edge of the Tibetan and western Chinese steppes. H. Weigold saw its tracks in the snow in January, caught one in a musk deer snare in July, and watched his dog chase another through thickets at an altitude of about 10,000 feet in the mountains east of Sungpan. The cat evidently stood its ground, because the dog returned with two bites, and it was in the same place the next day.

THE LEOPARD CAT (Plate 25)

We are on rather more knowledgeable terms with the beautiful leopard cat, which gained its scientific name *Felis bengalensis* because the original male specimen was picked up from the Hooghly River by a boat off Calcutta. It was kept alive and later mated with domestic cats. "One of its offspring had as little fear of water as its sire." Thomas Pennant, the famous eighteenth-century naturalist, was the first to describe it. It is a fairly big animal, the head and body making from one and one-half feet to nearly two and one-half feet, and the tail from nine inches to fourteen inches. Its English name witnesses to its leopard-like appearance: the body color is yellowish above, white below, though there are gray forms. The spots are solid rather than rosettes and are arranged in rows along the body, sometimes tending to merge into lines. This longitudinal pattern is said to be primitive and shows the cats' relationship to the civets.

There are a number of small streaks on the head and neck and the tail spots tend to form bands toward the black-tipped end. Rounded black ears with a white spot on the outer surface distinguish this and the next species from all other small cats.

The leopard cat is found almost throughout India in the mountain forests; northward it ranges to Kashmir, Baluchistan, and up to 50° N in Siberia; southeastward it is found in the forests and rubber plantations of Malaya and on some of the larger islands. It is nocturnal and feeds on small birds and mammals, including hares, and even mouse-deer, dropping on them from a tree like a leopard. It is the commonest cat in Borneo, coming into towns and villages after poultry, as it does in parts of India. Tom Harrisson, who has kept pet leopard cats, says they are commonly found in the great caves, where they scavenge the swiftlets that fall from their colonial nests high above in the dark. Frederick W. Champion actually photographed one hunting mice and showing the typical stance, forelegs stiff and straight, head up, back sloping away with the hindquarters close to the ground and the hind legs stretched out behind, apparently supporting nothing.

The leopard cat breeds in caves, under boulders, in hollow trees, even in nests built aboveground. The litter is three or four in India, two in Malaya, where Lim and Rahmin bin Omar believe there may be two in a year — in February or March and again in August or September. They kept two kittens found when about a month old in Selangor. At first very tame, they showed a change of temperament when about a year old, spitting at each other and growling when given food. They crouched in their cage by day and became restless at night. They reacted to a noise by lying flat on their bellies with ears lifted and front legs slightly raised, as though about to pounce. They fed themselves after six weeks and played with their prey like house cats. I wonder whether their eventual wildness was due to their being together, because the relatively friendly tradition established by the swimmer of the Hooghly River is supported by recent examples, including the beautiful animal photographed by E. P. Gee.

THE RUSTY-SPOTTED CAT (Plate 24)

Felis rubiginosa is a smaller animal, with a combined head and body length up to one and one-half feet and a tail of nine and one-half inches;

its weight is about three pounds. It has fawn upperparts and a white belly and is covered with lines of spots and bars rather like the leopard cat, of which it is a slighter edition. The marks are dark brown above, becoming more red on the flanks.

Its known distribution is southern India, where it does not seem to have been reported in recent years, as far north as the Central Provinces; but E. P. Gee has recently heard from the Maharajah of Bansda in Gujarat State that it is still common there and will be preserved. P. E. P. Deraniyagala, who described the Ceylon population as a distinct race in 1956, says it is "by no means common" now but is not shot for its skin because it is so small. It seems to live both in jungle and low scrub and grassland, running along drains in open country. Described as "elegant and agile," it hunts birds, including poultry, and small mammals by night, lying up by day in tree holes or under bushes. Litters of two or three are born in similar hidden sites. A tame one hunted for squirrels in the rafters of its home and attacked a gazelle fawn. It will hybridize with house cats.

TEMMINCK'S CAT (Plate 21)

Temminck's cat (*Felis temmincki*) corresponds to the golden cat of the African forests and is quite often to be seen in zoos, though this does not mean that its habits have ever been studied in the wild. The head and body combined may be from twenty-nine inches to thirty-four inches and the tail is about one and one-half feet. The typical coat is soft and full, a deep rich red above, paler below, and shows only faint stripes, except on the face, which has strong blackish and white streaks, the most prominent running from the eye to the neck. The color is extremely variable — black and gray examples are known — and the race inhabiting China is said to have strongly marked lines and rosettes over the body.

It has a wide range from eastern India and Nepal into Southeast Asia, including Sumatra, and northward through Tibet into China, and is divided into three fairly good races. Mr. Gee wrote an interesting note about the animal shown in Plate 21, and this summarizes almost all we know of its habits. It is evidently a forest animal, but is equally at home on the ground or in trees. Like many of its relatives, it lies up and breeds in cavities, especially hollow trees, and has litters of two or three. The natural prey may include small deer, but most records are limited to Temminck's cats that were shot when raiding domestic stock, even as big as a buffalo calf.

Gee bought his pet from a dealer in western Assam in April. It was one of three found in the Garo Hills in February, when it must have been very small. By November Tishi had grown into "a strikingly handsome and truly golden cat" and was devoted to his master, whom he regarded as "a sort of father and mother combined," suckling the lobes of his ears until discouraged, licking his head, and jumping onto his lap when he sat down. Tishi hunted in the forest up to a mile distant and even went into villages, but came back when called. He would play for hours with a house cat, with dogs, or by himself. His best trick was to catch a tennis ball six feet in the air and retrieve it. He was given to the London Zoo and has appeared on television.

THE FISHING CAT (Plate 24)

We come now to two specialized animals. The first is the rather mysterious fishing cat, *Felis viverrina*. It is a short-limbed, powerful cat, with a combined head and body length of from twenty-four inches to thirty-four inches and a tail ten to twelve inches long. It stands about sixteen inches at the shoulder and the weight ranges from seventeen pounds to nearly twenty-five pounds.

The body fur is "short, coarse, earthy-grey" infused with brown, according to the Bombay Natural History Society. It shows the pattern of dark spots and broken lines that we have seen in some of its relatives, with narrow streaks over the head and face. Marks on the limbs are not distinct, except for the two dark bars inside the forearm which most cats show; the tail is ringed with black.

The Indian distribution of the fishing cat is patchy, stretching westward through Bengal and the United Provinces to Sind; in peninsular India it is restricted to the Malabar coast between Mangalore and Cape Comorin, but it occurs in Ceylon. It is also found in Nepal, Burma, southern China, and in Southeast Asia, including Java and Formosa. In all these areas its haunts are thick jungle and scrub near water: reed beds, riversides, and tidal creeks. This suggests that it may live up to its name, but authorities are divided on the matter. George Tate admitted it prowled about reeds. The Bombay

Natural History Society report describes how it scoops up fish with a paw from a rock or overhanging bank — something that many other cats do — and takes freshwater mollusks. But it does not enter the water to hunt, though it has "moderately well-developed webs between the toes"; in its small claw sheaths it resembles the cheetah. Frederick W. Champion, the only man to photograph this, the leopard cat, and the jungle cat in the wild, says it leaves a very large track which can be mistaken for that of a young leopard.

Whatever doubts there may be about its fishing skill, there are plenty of accounts of its tackling animals as large as dogs, calves, and sheep; it has even carried off children, and a newly caught male broke into the next cage and killed a tame leopardess twice its size. These feats have led to its being considered untamable, but the early naturalist Blyth kept several males. Practically nothing is known of its breeding habits in the wild; a single kitten was found among the reeds in a den with runs leading to it.

PALLAS'S CAT (Plate 23)

Strangest of all the family is *Felis manul,* which, in spite of its small size, has some supporters for the honor of being the original Abominable Snowman, or Yeti. The combined length of head and body is from one and one-half feet to over two feet, with a tail of nine inches to one foot. The weight is from six pounds to seven and one-half pounds. Males may be rather larger than females.

The color of the whole animal is predominantly silvery gray, with long fur, especially on the underparts — perhaps an adaptation for sleeping or lying on snow-covered ground. The silvery appearance is due to the hairs of the back being black at base and tip and white in the middle. There sometimes are indistinct markings on the body and limbs and the end of the tail is ringed, with a black tip. But the most remarkable feature of Pallas's cat is the broad head with the low forehead and widely separated ears, a complete contrast to the serval. If we are right that the serval shows extreme adaptation to hunting by ear, then Pallas's cat is an example of specialization for hunting by eye in rocky mountainous country: it is able to peer over its hiding place without showing its ears. This and the long hair of the face, which suggests muttonchop whiskers, could give it an almost human appearance seen face to face but without the body showing.

There are three recognized races of this high-altitude cat: one in Turkestan and western Siberia, one in Mongolia and Siberia east of Lake Baikal, and a southern one (probably the smallest) in Tibet, where it has been seen up to almost 15,000 feet at Yamdrok Lake, and Ladakh. Though there are very few field observations, it is supposed to stalk picas (mouse hares) among the rocks; but it also lives in the steppes and deserts of China, hunting other small rodents. C. H. Stockley surprised one actually basking under a bush in sandhill country. Nothing is known of its breeding habits. Zoo specimens are not afraid of man and keep up a continual growl or hiss, which may be a form of purring; the mew, assumed to be a sexual call, is "a combination of the bark of a small dog and the hooting of an owl." When walking about, it carries the tail low with the tip curled up to show the dark underside.

THE CARACAL (African form shown on Plates 8, 9)

The next three species we have already met in Africa. The caracal is, or used to be, found in a wide area of central India and westward into Persia, Iraq, and Arabia, but there is very little information (a now familiar cry) about its habits in these countries. As in Africa, it is found in desert and open scrub, hunting birds, and mammals from rodents to small deer and antelopes. It has been popular in the role of a lesser cheetah trained for sport. The Gaekwar of Baroda used to keep a pack with which to hunt peafowl, hares, and other game. Caracals can also be trained to stalk and spring onto birds alone, and in Persia the best performers were able to kill up to ten pigeons out of a flock before they could leave the ground. There is an Indian record of one attacking a man, either by mistake or because it was very hungry.

THE JUNGLE CAT (Plate 22)

This species is much better known in Asia than in Africa. Several races cover its wide distribution, which extends from Burma through India and Ceylon to Iran, the Caspian area, and the lands bordering the eastern Mediterranean. It is found in dried grassland, scrub, and reed beds and often near villages, and is less nocturnal than most of the family, being seen about in mornings and evenings as it hunts a variety of birds and small mammals. It will snatch chickens in front of their owners; Thomas Jerdon was robbed by one of a peafowl he had just shot. It also tries conclusions with porcupines. Champion was able to approach hunting jungle cats quite easily by elephant but found it difficult to get a clear picture of them. He says they leave a very small track in proportion to their size. They tame easily but are suspicious of strangers.

THE INDIAN DESERT CAT

The African wildcat (see Plate 11) is known as the desert cat in India, where it seems to be a smaller animal, with head and body up to one and one-half feet and tail under a foot long. There is another race in Turkestan, but there has been a good deal of confusion about these small cats and we may not yet have reached a final position on their relationships. It does not seem to have been studied in India, where it ranges over the drier areas of the northwest, a similar habitat to that of the desert fox. According to fairly reliable reports it is said to prey on birds and rodents, especially gerbils, and one was killed while feeding on a sheep. It was hunted with greyhounds in crops and stubble.

THE LYNX

The lynx is the only cat with a distribution in Europe, Asia, and America. Formerly it was split into three or more species, but these are now generally regarded as races. As so little is known of its life and habits in Asia, I defer my main account of the lynx to the chapters on America and Europe. Lynxes do extend south to the upper valley of the Indus, where they are sandy gray. They remain at high altitudes and are said to attack sheep and goats.

THE EUROPEAN WILDCAT (Scottish form shown on Plates 4, 35)

Felis silvestris extends into Asia Minor and must therefore just be mentioned here, though I do not think it has been studied at all at the eastern end of its range.

Here, at another chapter's end, I am again appalled by the amount we have yet to learn about quite common and widespread animals. But are they all still common? What acute problems of conservation may be hidden in the jungles and mountains of this huge continent?

Cats of Africa.   Plate 5

above: Lion in figtree,
Queen Elizabeth National Park

right: Lioness showing underlying
spots, Nairobi National Park

Cats of Africa.   Plate 6

right: The leopon Reokichi, male of
the first family

middle: The leopons' parents, lioness
and leopard

below left: Reokichi

below right: The second leopon family

Leopard with kill (topi antelope) in tree

Cheetah cubs in first fur

A caracal, the African lynx

Cats of Africa. Plates 8, 9

opposite (Plate 9): Caracal kitten about six weeks old

Cheetah showing unsheathed claws

Cats of Africa.   Plate 10

Serval adults

The Small Cats of Africa.   Plate 11

top to bottom right: African wildcat
African golden cat in spotted coat
Black-footed cat
Sand cat

Serval kitten

Tiger lying up in daytime
Male tiger following female

opposite (Plate 13): Tiger about to spring
Tiger at night on trail

Cats of Asia.   Plate 14

Studies of an Indian tiger

Cats of Asia.   Plate 15

Indian lionesses with cubs in Gir Forest

Indian lion in Gir Forest

Cats of Asia. Plate 16

Indian lion at kill

ts of Asia. Plate 17

Night studies
of Indian leopards

Cats of Asia.   Plates 18, 19

opposite (Plate 18):
Snow leopard snarling

Close-up of snow leopard

Snow leopard, showing the thick fur

Marbled cat

Clouded leopard

Cats of Asia. Plate 21

Studies of Temminck's cat

Cats of Asia.   Plate 22

Field studies of jungle cats

Young jungle cat

Pallas's cat

Cats of Asia.   Plate 23

above: Bornean red cat
right: Chinese desert cat

Young flat-headed cat

Fishing cat

Smaller Cats of Asia. Plate 24

Rusty-spotted cat

Cats of Asia.   Plate 25

right: Leopard cat
right: Leopard cat hunting
below: Young leopard cat

Cats of America.   Plate 26

left: Puma at kill
below: Puma family

Cats of America.   Plate 27

top: Ocelot
middle: Jaguar
left: Jaguar, close-up

Cats of America. Plate 28

Two cats that are very difficult to distinguish
left: Margay
above and below: Little spotted cats

Young pampas cat

Geoffroy's cat

Andean cat

Kodkod,
black form

Small Cats of
South America.   Plate 29

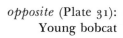

Cats of America.   Plates 30, 31

left: Jaguarundi, showing
otterlike form

below: Jaguarundi snarling

Cats of America. Plate 32

left: A treed bobcat
below: Bobcat in winter

Cats of America.   Plate 33. Canada lynx in close-up

Spanish lynx

Polish lynx hunting

Cats of Europe. Plate 34

left: Polish lynx, close-up

Cats of Europe.   Plate 35

right: Scottish wildcat, showing
the bushy tail

below: Scottish wildcats, male
on left, young female on right

Cats of Europe.   Plate 36

Three studies of house cats

right: My Ginger
left: After the hunt
below: Asleep

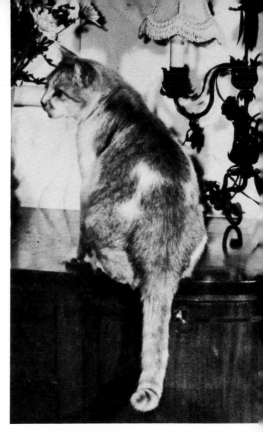

6. The Cats of North and South America

"To be seen at the Greay Hound Tavern in Roxbury, a wild creature, which was caught in the woods about eighty miles to the westward of this Town, called a Cattamount, it has a Tail like a Lyon, its Leggs are like a Bears, its Claws like an Eagle, its eyes like a Tyger, its countenance is a mixture of every Thing that is Fierce and Savage, he is exceedingly ravenous and devours all sorts of Creatures that he can come near; its Agility is surprising, it will Leap thirty Foot at one jump notwithstanding it is but Three months old. Whoever inclines to see this Creature may come to the Place aforesaid, paying a Shilling each, shall be welcome for their Money."

THE PUMA (Frontispiece, Plate 26)

This impressive buildup from the *Boston Gazette* of 1738 will serve to introduce the puma, mountain lion, cougar, panther, or "painter," or catamount, the red tiger of the Conquistadors, the bearer of a dozen Indian names, the "Mysterious American Cat" of Stanley P. Young and Edward A. Goldman's study *The Puma* (1946), and the North American Ghost of Bruce S. Wright's more recent study of *Felis concolor*. What has contributed to this reputation for mystery and savagery? As I have looked at the many books, articles, and references about it in scientific and popular literature, since Columbus first reported *leones* from Central America in 1502, I have come to the conclusion that the puma is still largely an unknown quantity even to the indefatigable Americans. Although it is the most widely distributed mammal in both continents of the New World — found even today over 100 degrees of latitude, from the deserts of Patagonia to the mountains of British Columbia — although hundreds of thousands have been hunted to death by man and his dogs since the coming of the Europeans, although I dare say the puma skins in museums if laid head to tail would stretch most of the way from New York to Chicago, no one has yet been able to watch pumas living their lives as we can watch lions in East Africa. Perhaps that would be expecting too much. I have already described the special conditions that lions now enjoy in the national parks and reserves. I think it is true that we know more about any of the big cats of the Old World than we do about the puma and jaguar — and this despite the great interest which many Americans and Canadians now take in their wildlife.

This is partly due to the use of different methods of hunting. Although luring to a bait is practiced in America, the much more common method is the pursuit with dogs. Indeed, Jay Bruce, a great hunter of the puma, revealed, after traveling 40,000 miles and killing nearly 700 of them, that all the living pumas he had seen except one had been after they were treed by his pack. Baiting a big cat does at least give you the chance to see it behaving for a short time more or less naturally, even if you then shoot it; hunting with dogs or trapping obviously do not. So all the lore which has accumulated in India, for example, as a result of shooting tigers and leopards from hides and machans is not paralleled for their American relatives.

A striking illustration of our ignorance about the puma is the confusion over its famous scream, "like a woman in agony." Let us set the scene with a much quoted story about early settlers on the Osage River, a tributary of the Mississippi.

> One day in early summer, Matthew Arbuckle rode into Papinsville. His horse was panting and flecked with foam. Matt told the group which gathered about him that, while plowing on his claim about a mile from the Osage, he had heard a terrible noise. He said it was something like the scream of a "painter," only ten times as long and loud. Uncle John Whitley, who had "fit with Jackson" at New Orleans and who was the acknowledged leader in that pioneer community, was sent for. He listened to Arbuckle and said the only thing to do was to get the hounds together, take the guns and go after the varmint, which he reckoned must have wandered down from the Rocky Range, as they called the Rocky Mountains

in those days. Uncle Jimmie Breckinridge seconded Captain Whitley, and the settlers got ready. As the posse was about to start for the trail a faint repetition of what Arbuckle had reported was heard. It was sure enough a new and terrifying sound. Uncle John at once remembered that his pretty daughter, Mattie, had gone on her pony to the river that morning.

"Ride, men!" shouted he. "Ride! Matt went down to the river, and I expect she's dead by this time." There was mounting in hot haste, but before the start was under way here came Mattie with her hair flying. She had heard the monster. Uncle John bade her get to the house and tell all of the women-folk to keep within doors. Darkness and storm came on together. Captain John Whitley led his party to Rock House, a cave forming a room twenty feet high, thirty feet wide, and forty feet deep. There was no disturbance in the night, but at daybreak that nerve-racking sound brought every man to his feet and set the hounds howling. The noise seemed to show that the monster was coming up the river and was near.

Uncle John posted his men for the encounter, every one behind a big tree. Four were told off with orders to have their knives ready and to wade in if the lead failed to stop the beast. Near Rock House was one of the sharpest bends of the scores of curves and bends of the Osage. Around the point and into view of the amazed settlers came slowly the "Flora Jones," the first steamboat to ascend the Upper Osage.

The whistle of a steam locomotive caused similar trouble in New York State about 1850. Young, who gives us the Osage story, also quotes a number of authorities over the past one hundred and thirty years with descriptions of the scream of the catamount. Theodore Roosevelt was convinced and claimed to have heard it, though his impression that "the animal seemed to be directly over my tent" surely suggests the sound came from a bird, probably a young horned owl, which can produce a really terrifying cry. Both the great Audubon and Ernest Thompson Seton, pioneer of real-life wildlife stories and a first-rate naturalist, were much more cautious. Seton pointed out the puma's repertoire was that of a house cat, magnified, but no more. In spite of its size, it is not one of the roaring cats, whose only American representative is the jaguar. William Beebe once heard a "loud, long drawn out quavering cry" from a puma in the Bronx Zoo, and Young himself heard a similar scream from the male of a pair at Denver. On the other hand, Robert Bean of the Chicago Zoo stated from long observation that all the females he had studied screamed but not the males, who utter a whistle, and that the scream only occurs at mating time. Jay Bruce never heard a puma scream, but that is not so surprising since his main concern was their destruction. Finally, Victor H. Cahalane, who mentions Bruce in *Mammals of North America,* heard a female in the Washington Zoo shriek repeatedly and comments: "I never heard a woman being murdered, but I think it is likely that she might be a whole lot more quiet about it." His conclusion, however, is that most "puma" screams heard in the wild are made by owls or lovelorn bobcats.

Well, if we should be fortunate enough to see this elusive, almost legendary animal, what does it look like? Its uniform color and lack of a mane make us think of a small lioness, but it is more sinuous in form and less stocky. The summer coat is generally a reddish brown, rather darker along the ridge of the back and the tail, which sometimes has a black tip but of course no tuft — that is the prerogative only of Leo. The underparts shade into white on the throat, breast, and belly. The head is noticeably rounder than that of most other cats and the face gets its "expression" from dark lines above the eyes and on either side of the upper lip, which is almost white; the ears are short and rounded. In winter the upperparts become grayish or mouse-brown. Cubs when born are buff-colored, with black spots and a ringed tail, reminding us again of true lions, but the arrangement of the spots roughly in lines is different. They gradually disappear, although sometimes may be seen faintly under the adult coat.

Body color varies, as with other cats, between individuals as well as from region to region. The pumas of the tropics are said to be relatively smaller and brighter than those of Patagonia or North America. But to a good splitter this is a terrible simplification! Goldman describes thirty subspecies. The ranges of the fourteen North American races adjoin, apart from the interesting population on Vancouver Island, and the slender distinctions between them admittedly shade into each other. However, several of the South American races are apparently quite isolated and include the type Linnaeus first described more than two hundred years ago, from Cayenne of French Guiana. Black or blackish individuals occur in the southern continent, but, like black panthers, they are simply melanistic forms, not a separate race.

Pumas also vary greatly in size. The tail is about half the length of head and body combined and may be from under two to about three feet long; the record total length is just under nine and one-half feet; but many full-grown males are only six feet to seven feet. Females are usually a good deal smaller, though the two sexes overlap in length and in shoulder height, which may be from under two feet to two and one-half feet. Females weigh from 135 pounds down to half that or less; I think the male record is still the 227-pounder shot by Theodore Roosevelt in Colorado, if we discount a monster from Arizona supposed to have scaled 276 pounds after its intestines had been removed! At the other extreme, Arizona provided an old male, estimated at eight to twelve years, and only weighing forty-six pounds. The normal male range seems to be from about eighty to 140 pounds.

The puma has been wonderfully tenacious over its wide distribution. When Young and Goldman wrote this book in 1946 they summarized its history in each state of the United States and, though a lot of the information was rather vague, it looked as if pumas were still found regularly in twelve western and southern states, where recruitment from Mexico could be an important factor. In 1959 Bruce S. Wright gave his opinion that the puma was "present, as either a transient or a permanent resident, in almost every state from the Canadian border to Florida." Until he made his thorough investigation, following up every clue with a host of correspondents, recent sightings of pumas in eastern North America had largely been discounted. But he quotes many records from seven states and three Canadian provinces, especially Maine and New Brunswick. He describes methods of recording tracks, scrapes, and droppings and how to deduce details of the animals from them.

Mexico is regarded as a stronghold of the puma. In Central and South America, although the distribution is not now continuous — perhaps it never was — it extends to the Strait of Magellan. So, quite apart from its legendary qualities, the puma shows a remarkable physical adaptation to the whole gamut of climates to be found in the New World: subarctic in the Peace River district of Canada, alpine at 13,000 feet in the Rocky Mountains, temperate, subtropical, tropical, temperate again through to subantarctic. And within this great variation no habitat seems to come amiss: mountain, forest, desert, scrub, swamp, and jungle, though it is perhaps less at home in the last than the jaguar. I have noticed that such adaptability is rather characteristic of the more successful predators, birds as well as mammals.

Another feature of the successful predator is that all is grist to his mill. The puma will eat anything from slugs to horses; but its favorite prey is deer and it prospers best where deer are numerous. Since it has been said there are now more deer and Indians on Cape Cod than when the Pilgrim Fathers arrived, it may be that the puma's reappearance in the eastern United States is a result of this abundance.

Victor H. Cahalane has depicted vividly the final moments of a stalk.

> *Only sixty feet away a buck [mule deer] picks at a seedling manzanita. Immediately the cougar's muscles, like taut steel springs, release the pent-up energy. A swift, cold fury, she makes two tremendous leaps, then a final short one. The victim has only time to hear a rushing sound and to throw up his head. Then he is struck by the avalanche. With more than one hundred pounds of weight behind them, the great forepaws strike the deer's shoulder. They drive the front quarters violently away. The head and neck snap around against the cougar's body. Like a sack of bones and flesh the deer crashes to earth fully twenty feet off. He is dead, the neck broken.*

The kill may be the result of a long search and hunt, up to twenty-five miles in a night, which is the puma's most active time — another reason for our lack of firsthand observations. In walking, the hind paw, with its smaller central pad, is placed partly on top of the front paw mark; the tail swings from side to side, making characteristic marks in snow. The puma leaves a straight track, unlike the zigzags of the bobcat, has regular scratching places for its claws, and tidily buries its feces, sometimes in a latrine area which is used repeatedly. On the trail it can go for a long time without drinking.

Pumas hunt by sight and smell, though their nose is not as keen as that of the dog family. When game is in view, they begin a stealthy approach, like a lion — or a house cat for that matter — until within striking distance, when the final attack is made as Cahalane describes it. Sometimes only a single spring is needed; a South African puma was credited with one of more than forty feet, which, if true, would support a claim that it is the most agile of all cats. If the prey does not collapse at once, the killer hangs on, throwing its weight against the animal; the coup de grâce seems to be a bite in the neck. But eyewitness accounts of kills are few. A Canadian professor saw a puma leap onto the back of a mountain goat in the hills near Banff, Alberta, and the famous Daniel Boone told how he and his brother saw one on the back of a large buffalo, clawing it and causing the whole herd to stampede. Boone with his trusty flintlock "displaced the monster from its seat," the usual end of cougar stories.

There is no doubt that animals bigger than the attacker are successfully brought down, even full-grown horses. One hunter woke at the end of a night in a hut to find that a puma had killed his tethered mount after a terrific struggle. Cattle, goats, and especially sheep are taken and, like the leopard in Africa, the puma may run riot and massacre the wretched confined animals: 192 bedding ewes in a single night seems to be the record from Colorado. Of course, in nature such opportunities do not occur and the puma cannot be blamed for reacting to what students of animal behavior call a supranormal stimulus.

In North America the white-tailed deer is probably the most frequent wild prey because it occupies the puma's preferred habitat of mountain woodland; but other kinds are killed when the chance occurs, including the American elk, or wapiti, a close relative of the Old World red deer, and several South American species of deer. Near the southern limit of its range the guanaco, a relative of the llama, used to be favored, and a full list of the mammals recorded as its victims would be long indeed. It seems to deal with porcupines better than its Old World cousins, turning them over on their backs and ripping their bellies open. If quills get into its paws, it is apparently — or so it is said — able to pull them out with its teeth. Even mice are hunted under logs, game birds and fish may be taken at times, and there is the curious story of "snail"-eating in British Columbia. Young thinks this refers to a large yellow slug. It is known that house cats sometimes form addictions to slugs, even though they cause vomiting.

There are records of pumas killing or eating other predatory mammals: martens, skunks, raccoons, foxes, even coyotes. But there is no active cannibalism. Occasionally a puma will eat part of a dead mate. The eating of his own family by an insensitive father of course is common in the animal world.

None of the New World cats is nearly so much of a danger to man as are lions, tigers, and leopards. The puma, in fact, may be said to survive by making himself scarce when man appears, though he will occasionally follow humans out of curiosity. Most stories of attacks turn out to be merely stories, but there are one or two well-authenticated cases of man-eating. For example, an unfortunate boy in Washington state in 1924; and there is the tombstone of Philip Tanner in Pennsylvania, dated 1751, with a rough carving of a puma on it. Tanner was killed quite close to the grave-yard. Other attacks are supposed to be due to rabies or literally to mistaken identity, because the man was dressed in furs. Bruce S. Wright says that cubs may be dangerous when first deserted by the mother and desperately hungry. There have been several recent accounts of attacks by animals of this age on Vancouver Island, where the isolated population may in any case find food hard to come by.

Having killed, the puma settles down to the sort of feasting routine we have met before. It usually opens the belly and removes the intestines, burying or covering them over. But it is fond of some of the smaller organs, and the liver is a particular delicacy. Next, the ribs and loins are eaten. The first meal may amount to six or seven pounds of meat and entrails. The carcass is then buried, sometimes quite deep, and the puma retires to sleep it off. A second meal is usual, and if the kill keeps fresh the puma may return again and again, until there is practically nothing left. However, more choosy than the true lion, it does not like carrion. Mothers bring their families to join in, and occasionally the father takes a share. Like its Old World relatives, the puma is credited with remarkable feats of haulage when the place of killing does not make a suitably safe dining room.

Sometimes it only takes a drink of blood and leaves its prey to coyotes and bears; it is then accused of killing for pleasure.

How often does a puma kill, not counting the sort of orgies among domestic stock I have mentioned? Cahalane estimates between thirty-five and one hundred times a year, depending on the size of the prey and the animals' movements. A puma on the run before dogs will go on killing, more frequently perhaps than usual because it cannot return to its kills. There is some evidence that it weeds out abnormal animals in deer herds and plays a useful part in control of their numbers. If not pursued, its range is about twelve miles, but it will move if game becomes scarce. A cub that Clark Gable tried to keep as a pet escaped and was found a year later seventy-five miles away. There are no strict territories among males, but females tend to hunt for their litters close to the den; one with a full-grown kitten ranged over six square miles in Oregon.

Pumas breed when two to three years old. The male indicates by scratchings in the bare earth that he is ready to mate. The honeymoon lasts about two weeks; during this time the male will fight rivals to the death. Passion spent, the pair only meet casually and even hostilely, though there are recorded exceptions. The gestation period is ninety-six days and most litters are born in the North American spring or in August. D. J. Brand noted no special season for births in zoos, where litters are from two to four, usually three. One to six are recorded in the wild, but not more than two or three survive. The kittens, or cubs, are born furry but blind; they are about a foot long and weigh about a pound. After nine or ten days they begin to romp like any other kittens and come out of the den, which is in a cavern or dense brushwood. They begin to eat meat at six to seven weeks, when they weigh about ten pounds, and go out with their mother to kills a week or two later. At eight months they are four or five feet long and weigh up to fifty pounds, but they are not really independent until they are about two years old and ready to start their own breeding cycle. They are lucky in the wild if they live to be twelve, but in zoos they may go on another six years. Man is, of course, their only serious enemy once they have passed childish hazards, though the occasional hunt may go wrong and a wound from a desperate stag may turn septic. Fights with jaguars may occur naturally, and the more agile puma is backed to win.

Young pumas are by far the most playful of all young cats, big or small; and play does not end with childhood; an adult has been watched "rolling over and over in the shade of a tree, scratching itself against the trunk, curling its tail and acting like an overgrown tomcat." This puts the ghost of North America in a less terrifying light.

Unfortunately, until recently few men have been content simply to watch such entertaining scenes: they have been the puma's implacable foe. I mentioned briefly in Chapter 1 the ring hunts with beaters of the Inca kings. These were primarily economic in their object: they were held as a great roundup after the breeding season of the guanacos and vicuñas on which the Peruvians were dependent for wool and meat. An army of 30,000 men spread out into an enormous circle tens of miles in diameter and then closed in until thousands of animals were enclosed. All the predators, including the pumas, were killed, but a breeding stock of the valuable animals was released and the area was rested for three years before the next drive.

The bolas are the traditional hunting weapon of the South American Indian, and when he became a horseman, after the arrival of the Europeans, he was better able to come to terms with the puma in the open savannah and bring it down with a dexterous throw of the whirling stones. In Mexico pumas and other predatory animals were lured at night by ingenious imitation of the bleating of deer or goats and then shot by lantern light. A widespread but much less sporting method was the pit, often furnished with a bait animal which was "left in discomfort so that it would squeal intermittently." The bottom of the pit might be fitted with stakes to ensure the discomfort of the trapped animal too. In British Guiana a large box trap was used, with the bait in a separate compartment.

Hunting with dogs has been a favorite method in North America for many years; it is at least an energetic sport, involving an element of risk to the hunter. But most pumas taken under "control programs," as they are euphemistically called in game and livestock areas, are trapped. Young admitted that "although some persons oppose the use of such traps as inhumane no better or more practical device is yet available." I am afraid I must be counted among these persons, especially when I learn that "jaws are adjusted to fit snugly and closely."

Of course, great ingenuity and knowledge of the puma's habits are needed to get results. Traps are usually set near scratch hills or kills, or along frequented trails, where small obstacles are provided so that the animal steps daintily over them and onto the platform of the trap. Sometimes oil of catnip is used as an attraction. Young gives detailed instructions for making a "lasting lure" with it, but it is only fair to say that he and Tappan Gregory also used catnip when getting pumas to photograph themselves — ten years after Frederick Champion's success with the Indian tiger. The first puma photographs in the wild were taken by Frank M. Chapman on Barro Colorado in the Panama Canal Zone in the 1920's, using a trip-wire technique.

I do not intend to dwell on means of destruction; this is a book about living animals. Fortunately the puma seems able to withstand "control" and it is gradually being recognized that it and other carnivores are themselves a valuable check on the numbers of game animals, ensuring the survival of the fittest. With domestic livestock it is different, and no doubt the long guerrilla war will continue in those areas where cattle and sheep are all-important.

In spite of a reputation for unreliability the puma is a popular animal in captivity. There were two cubs at the London Zoo in 1832. They are particularly appealing in their first spotted coats, except when they go native at the sight of fresh liver or other meat. Traditional prey, such as goats or chickens, also arouse them, but they may become friendly with dogs and other pets. Pumas, like ourselves, have individual temperaments. Cahalane mentions a sullen female in the Washington Zoo which only reacted favorably to a certain lady visitor. I wonder what they said to each other.

THE JAGUAR (Plates 3, 27)

The other big cat of the New World, *Panthera onca*, we may consider as the counterpart of the leopard. It and the leopard are probably descended from a quite recent common ancestor, whereas the puma has no near living relations, though some extinct species resemble it. The jaguar's rosette spots with dark centers on the tawny-yellow ground color are fewer and larger than the leopard's, though they tend to concentrate along the back. There are irregular black spots on the pale underparts and rings around the lower half of the tail. The face is unstriped, with a black mark on the lower jaw by the mouth; the backs of the ears are black. The coat color varies, from almost white to black forms on which the spots are hardly visible.

Males and females look alike, though differing in size, the female averaging about a fifth smaller than the male. Measurements and weights overlap the puma's, but the jaguar is generally rather bigger and heavier, and therefore, according to most authorities, less agile. Full-grown animals range from a total length of five and one-half to nine feet, of which two to two and one-half feet may be tail. They stand two and one-quarter to two and one-half feet at the shoulder. Weights have been recorded from 125 pounds to double that, equivalent to a tiger rather than a leopard. The largest specimens come from Brazil.

The distribution of the jaguar has always been much more restricted than that of the puma. Indeed it is probably not much less extensive now than when Europeans first came to America. It just reaches the Southwest in the United States, then, divided into several geographical races, stretches through the subtropical and tropical zones to Argentina. The jaguar, like the leopard, is an animal of thick cover and is a good climber, so it prefers jungles and swamps. Nevertheless, it also comes into the open savannahs and deserts in the northern and southern parts of its range.

A. Starker Leopold, who studied it in Mexico, found that it usually kept to a territory, an area of two to five square miles; hence the saying, "each hill has its own tiger." Occasionally one wanders off, like the jaguar which traveled 500 miles only to be killed in Baja California in 1955; "such vagrants," says Leopold, "seem to adopt travel as a way of life, like itinerant Englishmen." Although I am not English, I at times feel a lot of sympathy with these wanderers.

On the move the jaguar's pugmarks are four to five inches across, the forepaw being larger than the hind, and it can be recognized with experience. The jaguar has no fear of water, which the puma on the whole avoids, and swims well. It does most of its stalking on the ground, but may chase monkeys, who have a particular fear of it, and parrots in the trees. Like the tiger it is not always a silent hunter, often grunting *uh uh uh* as it goes. After a leopard-like stalk the final attack is a lightning bound and crippling blow; but if this fails, the jaguar does not follow its intended victim. The kill may be buried or left in the open, probably according to the type of ground, between visits.

Peccaries, the wild hog's relatives in South and Central America, are often quoted as the jaguar's favorite prey, but we may fairly call its diet catholic: it will hunt deer, tapirs, capybaras — the largest rodents in the world — agoutis, sloths, wild turkeys, and other birds. Living so often in wetlands, it is also a fish-eater, and, although the cat family's conventional method of fishing is to lie along an overhanging bough or bank and scoop the water, it has been seriously suggested that the jaguar may use its tail, presumably as a sort of bait. But what happens in a river infested with piranhas, those carnivorous fish that can strip a limb of flesh in a few seconds? I find it easier to believe that jaguars immobilize turtles by turning them onto their backs, and eat their eggs; they are also known to kill small alligators and crocodiles. Like other big cats, they cannot resist domestic stock when they get the chance: small cattle and horses, pigs, and dogs — a taste shared with the leopard.

The South American writer Azara records a jaguar's dragging a horse seventy yards to a river and towing it across. Alexander von Humboldt, the German who explored South America at the beginning of the last century, saw a huge jaguar lying under a zaman tree with a capybara under one paw, and a crowd of vultures in the offing. When Humboldt's boat approached, the jaguar hid and the vultures moved in. This was too much for the owner, which reappeared, "leapt into the midst of them and, in a fit of rage, expressed by his gait and the movements of his tail, carried off his prey into the forest. Humboldt also recorded that a jaguar fled when a child, with whom it had been playing, struck it; and there is no suggestion that it is ever a serious menace to man, except from Azara who said that when attacking a camp the jaguar first took the dog, next the Negro, then the Indian, and finally the Spaniard.

An earlier story recounts how the Indian inhabitants of Tumbes released a lion (puma) and tiger (jaguar) as the Greek knight Pedro de Candia walked toward the town from Pizarro's ship. To their surprise, the big cats simply crouched at his feet and he gave the Indians to understand that the Cross which he held was the cause of this miracle. Perhaps his brave action is the reason why there has not been a man-eating problem on the American continent!

Although the jaguar is one of the big five roaring cats, it does not seem to make use of its potential any more than the leopard. The deep grunting already described is its best-known utterance; it snarls and growls when cornered, and the male has a mewing cry — perhaps used in the mating season — which has been imitated to lure jaguars to their deaths. They will also come to baits, being less particular than pumas about carrion, and are extensively hunted with dogs, showing more fight at bay than pumas usually do. In open country they are or were ridden down and speared, as lions were in the heyday of British India.

Like other big cats, jaguars are extensively kept in zoos, but are considered unreliable. D. G. Elliot, the first monographist of the cat family, thought they were untamable. But they breed well enough and D. J. Brand gives a gestation period of 95 to 108 days and an average litter of two cubs.

Wild births take place around January in the northern part of the jaguar's range; there is probably no fixed breeding season in the tropics. Male and female only come together at mating time, when, indeed, gatherings of eight suitors have been recorded. The mother does all the rearing of the litter. Usually two and sometimes four cubs are born; they arrive furred but with eyes closed and come out of the well-hidden den after about two weeks. They stay with their mother for about two years, when they are mature and able to breed in their turn.

THE OCELOT (Plate 27)

If it seems that comparatively little is known about the life history of such an important member of the family as the jaguar, we plunge from now on into even greater obscurity with the smaller cats of Central and South America, though the ocelot has many supporters for Cahalane's claim that it is the handsomest of all. It has also the best reputation for docility, in spite of its alternative names of leopard cat and tiger cat and the fact that a vegetarian diet is recommended for captives. Recently, however, Lester E. Fisher has said he has yet to see a sweet-natured ocelot. Alexander Wilson, the pioneer American naturalist, kept one that playfully attacked a small child and tore up a chamois leather glove. Another paid its way as a ship's cat, leaping three yards onto astonished rats. It was gentle with the crew, even sleeping with them in their hammocks and racing them via the shrouds to the top of the masts. Alas, the ocelot was lost overboard, apparently mistaking flying fish for birds and being unable to resist them.

Unhappily, ocelot fur is much prized for coats and collars, and it is wonderfully variable. The extreme ground colors are grayish and cinnamon; on them is imposed what E. Raymond Hall and Keith R. Kelson describe as dark markings forming chainlike streaks of black-bordered elongated spots that run obliquely down the sides. The head has small black spots and two black stripes on each cheek; there are four or five parallel black stripes on the neck. The ground color of the sides is paler than the back, and the underparts are almost white. The upper side of the tail is marked with dark bars or blotches. This beautiful animal is forty to fifty inches long, of which twelve to fifteen inches is tail. It stands up to one and one-half feet at the shoulder and the weight range is from twenty-five to thirty-five pounds, females being about a fifth smaller than males.

Felis pardalis is still found in the extreme southern United States, in Arizona and Texas, and it extends through the tropics to Ecuador and northern Argentina, a range similar to the jaguar's. It is an inhabitant of forest, or at least thick cover, and is an excellent climber, moving mostly by night but sometimes by day. D. G. Elliot said that ocelots liked to lie up in *Opuntia* scrub on the lower Rio Bravo, their coats picking up many prickles, which lodged horizontally and soon fell out. They also sleep on tree branches.

As we might expect, ocelots hunt a whole range of medium-sized and small mammals and birds: rabbits, rodents, and porcupines — which sometimes leave their quills as a memento — deer fawns, agoutis, monkeys, and tree lizards. They can manage livestock from chickens and guinea-fowl to pigs, dogs, lambs, and young calves. In the United States they have killed snakes, and since they swim well they may take fish. When hunted for such crimes they often double back on their tracks; in traps they await their fate patiently.

This model creature also has a superior domestic life to most of its relatives: pairs remain together, communicating with mewing cries, and in captivity several will live peaceably in the same cage. They have special latrine mounds, as do many other carnivores. There is probably no fixed breeding season in the tropics, but usually in Texas the two kittens are born during the autumn in a rocky den or hollow log; they look like their parents from birth, but are rather darker. A. Starker Leopold says ocelots in Yucatán, Mexico, mate in October and breed in January.

At the chimpanzee farm in Florida of which I was long the director, we had a particularly handsome pet ocelot — tame, playful, and even at times affectionate, but always nervous and prone to sudden panic. It lived in a large disused aviary, sleeping most of the day in one of the comfortable nesting-boxes. One day I noticed it pacing up and down restlessly, in evident extreme alarm, and nothing we could do would calm its fear. Several hours after the ocelot had begun its frantic pacing we received a hurricane warning — all too frequent an occurrence in Florida — and we started on our hurricane routine, moving all the chimpanzees, the monkeys, the birds to the shelters provided for these emergencies. All our efforts to catch the terrified ocelot failed, and since it became unsafe to continue to work in the open I finally decided that it probably would be better off in its familiar nesting-box than in the strange and crowded surroundings of the shelters. Next day, when the hurricane had passed, leaving a wake of destruction, the old aviary and the nesting-boxes were undamaged; but the beautiful ocelot, who had in some mysterious way known that disaster was coming, lay dead on the floor of the aviary.

THE MARGAY (Plate 28)

Felis wiedi is a smaller edition of the ocelot, and is so rare in North America that only two were taken by Edward A. Goldman and E. W. Nelson in a collection of 15,000 Mexican mammals. Leopold only knew two more records of the *"tigrillo."* Its status as an animal of the United States rests on a specimen from Eagle Pass in Maverick County, Texas. The range extends to southern Brazil and Bolivia. Azara found them common in Paraguay in the last century, though there has been a good deal of confusion between them and other small to medium-sized cats, especially the one described next.

The biggest male margays compare with ocelots at thirty-five pounds. Nor is there much in it with their measurements. Males go up to more than four feet in length, of which twenty inches is tail; females up to three and one-half feet, but they are usually slimmer, with a relatively longer tail. Glover M. Allen described a gray type from Mexico, with tawny forms to the south; in Nicaragua the underparts, usually whitish, are yellow. The black markings are "narrow, linear, sharply defined, occasionally encircling patches of ground color." There are rows of large oval blotches across the thighs and vertical bands on the shoulders, but the underparts are not spotted.

Practically nothing is known about the margay's life in the wild. We infer from its large, dark eyes that it hunts by night and lies up in the trees, for it is another forest animal, by day. It is believed to prey on rodents, rabbits, birds, and occasionally on chickens; tame ones have hunted rats and mice. Azara said it entered stockyards on dark nights and killed up to six hens at a time. He also believed it had one or two cubs in a litter and was easily domesticated. He has a charming story of fourteen that slept in a ball — when one wanted to stretch it licked the next one. They cut up straw for bedding. Rather surprisingly — but so the unhappy story goes — they were given live house cats to eat. These they seized by the nape and lay neatly on top of, "not permitting them to stir" until they died. The cats took their revenge by disagreeing internally with the margays, as did frogs and toads. Birds were fastidiously plucked before being eaten. In recent times margays have been kept in the Arizona-Sonora Desert Museum at Tucson, Arizona, and even in city apartments.

THE LITTLE SPOTTED CAT (Plate 28)

For the little spotted cat *(Felis tigrina)*, whose range is from Costa Rica into northern South America, I have little more than a description, and some measurements: its total length is only from two and one-half to three and one-quarter feet, of which ten to seventeen inches may be tail. Larger individuals are confused with margays, a situation not assisted by the variety of both scientific and popular names. The coat is normally yellowish, shading to white on the underparts; there is an interrupted dark line down the ridge of the back and the markings along the flanks break up into rosettes with dark tawny centers as they approach the heavily ringed tail. The belly and limbs are spotted, but the spots fade out down the legs. There is a rather striking white line above the eyes and indistinct black lines elsewhere on the face; the backs of the ears have white spots at the base. There are two well-marked black lines on the neck. This small cat was first exhibited in London as coming from India. It is sometimes kept in American zoos, but makes a poor captive and is apt to bite. It is an inhabitant of thick woodland, is a good climber, and preys on the usual birds and rodents.

THE JAGUARUNDI (Plate 30)

The most distinctive of the smaller cats is the variously spelled jaguarundi, which in spite of its name looks nothing like a jaguar. In fact, it shows a remarkable approach to the mustelids, that important family of carnivores including the otters, badgers, martens, and weasels. It has an elongated body with a long, low head and small ears, and the upperparts are unspotted, varying from blackish or brownish gray to chestnut-red and tawny. The brown form is known as the eyra, and was for some time considered to be a different species. The gray form becomes darker in winter.

The total length varies from just under three feet to more than four feet, of which the long tail accounts for one and one-half feet or more; the shoulder height is low, only ten to twelve inches, and weights run from ten to twenty pounds.

Felis yagouarundi is another marginal animal in the United States just extending into the Southwest, and it has become rare since the cutting of the thickets in the delta of the Rio Grande. Southward its range runs through the tropics to Paraguay. Although its form suggests a life mainly on the ground, it is regarded as a forest and swamp animal and swims so well that in parts of Mexico it is known as the otter-cat. Its favorite North American habitat is dense chaparral scrub near water.

Weasel-like, jaguarundis are active all round the clock, though supposed to be mainly nocturnal in the tropics; but F. B. Armstrong said they were often about and could be seen drinking at ponds in the middle of the day. They have favorite trails on the ground which are used when hunting a variety of small mammals and birds through the thickest cover. C. F. Garmer, who kept a pet one, said it was particularly fond of game birds — quails, chachalacas, guans, and wild turkeys — and could become a pest in the hen run. Jaguarundis are trapped along their trails, or hunted with dogs, when they run up trees and hide in the bromeliads growing on the trunks. At night they are shot by deer hunters, who pick up their shining eyes with lights.

During his survey of Mexican wildlife, A. Starker Leopold came across only one jaguarundi, along the Rio Salto in eastern San Luis Potosí province. "A long reddish form darted across a narrow trail ahead of me and into a thicket of palmettos. It was not seen again."

Jaguarundis are solitary except at mating time. In Mexico this takes place in November and December, and is accompanied by a lot of caterwauling and fighting. Usually two, but up to four, kittens are born nine or ten weeks later in a hollow tree or other hideout. There may be two litters a year in some areas, because young have been reported both in March and August. They are unspotted at birth, and gray and brown animals may occur in the same litter.

THE PAMPAS CAT (Plate 29)

Darwin knew the pampas cat, now scientifically called *Felis colocolo,* by its former name of *F. pajeros,* which he pointed out was derived from the word *paja* meaning "straw," because it lived in reed beds. It is a wide-ranging species in South America, occurring over some fourteen hundred miles from north to south, mainly in Argentina. About the size of a house cat, it has a total length rather over two feet, of which a foot may be tail.

In general it is a silvery-gray animal, with narrow stripes of reddish brown running obliquely along its back and flanks and a dark line down the center of the back. There are faint stripes behind and below the eyes and reaching to the ears, which are a dark reddish brown behind. The underparts are whitish, with bright brown bars; the long tail is gray. A gray, almost unmarked form also occurs.

When Elliot wrote his monograph in 1883, the name *F. colocolo* had been given by Molina to a supposedly distinct species called Molina's Guiana cat, based apparently on a single specimen in a collection at Milan. Unlike the typical pampas cat, this animal and another young male captured in 1869 for the Santiago Zoo in Chile had black rings round the tail. Further confusion was caused because *colocolo* is really the name of a marsupial. As recently as 1940 Cabrera and Yepes believed there were two distinct species, the *Gato pajero* in the south, and the *kudmu* of the Araucano Indians in the north. Whatever the rights of the matter, this seems the place to quote a story from Griffith's *Animal Kingdom* about a presumed Guiana cat, a fierce animal shot in the interior by an officer of Lewinstein's riflemen, stuffed, and sent to England as a present to the Duke of York. It was placed on the awning of a boat descending the Paramaribo, which in places was overhung by tall trees full of resting monkeys. "No sooner was the stuffed specimen in sight than the whole community would troop off with prodigious screams and howlings," though normally the passing of the boat "excited but little incident." After all this, it is believed that the terror of the monkeys failed to reach the noble duke for whom it was intended.

Very little is known of the pampas cat, which is now probably extinct in Uruguay and rare in Argentina because of the devastating invasion of civilization. It is said to be nocturnal, to inhabit low dense thickets, and to feed on birds and small mammals, especially guinea pigs. Its relatively short claws suggest a life mainly on the ground. The one, two, occasionally three kittens look like their parents from birth.

GEOFFROY'S CAT (Plate 29)

Another largely Argentinian feline is Geoffroy's cat (*Felis geoffroyi*), supposed to range from the Rio Grande do Sul to Santa Cruz in Patagonia and into southwestern Bolivia. It is a robust animal with a relatively big head, and may be over three feet long, fifteen inches being tail. Gray and brown forms occur, marked with wavy black streaks and lines, and the fur is sought after locally. The tail is ringed; the face is patterned with thin lines and the ears are black and brown behind.

It is a cat of mountainous country, haunting patches of scrub, especially near the salinas in the interior of Argentina. It is an excellent climber, hunting birds and small mammals in the trees, whose branches it uses for rest and ambush, like a miniature jaguar. Geoffroy's cat avoids human settlement, except isolated ranches which it may raid for chickens. A litter of two or three kittens, which resemble their parents, is produced once a year in a well-hidden den of dead leaves.

THE KODKOD (Plate 29)

The curiously named kodkod (*Felis guigna*) lives on the edge of the Cordilleras in Chile, chiefly in the provinces of Cautín, Valdivia, and Aysén, but does not come down to the Patagonian tableland. It is another woodland species, hunting small mammals, climbing expertly and hiding in the trees, where it is quite invisible. It is a distinctively patterned little cat, its black markings reduced to lines of small spots along the back and flanks; the tail is heavily ringed with black. There are a few markings on the face, and the underparts are light with a prominent blackish-brown band across the throat. The total length is only about two and one-quarter feet, of which nine inches is tail.

Unlike most of its relations, it was studied by R. A. Philippi at Valdivia, where it was abundant in the middle of the last century. While its normal prey are rodents, groups used to visit the city at night to steal chickens and meat, and as many as twenty of these raiders were killed in one morning. They included some melanistic individuals. More recently, a series of eight were taken seventy-five miles north of Valdivia in 1910–1911, and it is from these our description and measurements come.

THE ANDEAN CAT (Plate 29)

At even higher levels lives the Andean cat (*Felis jacobita*), a larger animal with a total length up to four feet, of which the tail is one and one-half feet. It is found in the mountainous areas of northwestern Argentina, Bolivia, Peru, and northern Chile, living on arid rocky slopes, where it hunts chinchillas and vizcachas. It is a grayish animal, with brown streaks and bars down its flanks, bands round its bushy gray tail, and a rather prominent nose — perhaps it hunts more by scent than other cats. Nothing seems to be known of the breeding habits of this or the preceding species.

THE BOBCAT (Plates 31, 32)

The two lynxes have accumulated much fatter dossiers than the cats of tropical America. The bobcat — named from "it's impudent and abbreviated tail," as Cahalane calls it — or bay lynx — from its color — is also often called the wildcat, which seems to be a tribute to its character. By repute it is as difficult to tame as the wildcat of Europe, and yet it lives closer to Western civilization than any other member of the family and is a remarkable example of how quite a large carnivorous animal can survive on the edge of cities, as the fox and badger do in England.

A typical *Felis rufa* is reddish brown above, the color being most intense along the top of the back, and shading to white underneath. In the arid Southwest of the United States and in Mexico it is pale brown, and other varieties occur; sometimes the dark streaks and spots overlaying the ground color are absent. The short tail has rather indistinct rings, and the lower part of it is black above, white beneath — a small point separating it from the Canada lynx, which I am going to call simply the lynx. The long tufted ears are black behind, with a white spot near the tip, and there are white and dark stripes on the face; the feet, though large, do not compare with those of its relative the lynx, and are less hairy. Males on the whole are bigger than females but measurements overlap. The total length of males ranges between thirty-two and fifty inches, of which five to seven and one-half inches are tail; females are from twenty-eight inches to four feet, with tails four to seven inches. The shoulder height is from twenty inches to about two feet. At a year old bobcats weigh eight to twelve pounds, but may reach twenty-five pounds when fully mature.

The bobcat is still found pretty much throughout the United States well into Canada, and in most of Mexico, showing in miniature the puma's tolerance of climates and habitats: it is at home in woods, thickets, and swamps, in deserts, broken country, and high into the hills. But it prefers a mixed terrain to dense forest, and Cahalane says it increased in the state of Minnesota as lumbering opened up the country, from an estimated population of 1800 to about 4000.

Like the puma, the bobcat owes its success partly to its wraithlike behavior — where it exists on the outskirts of the towns, people often do not know it is there. Another factor is that it preys on small animals which have also adapted themselves to suburban life. Of course it is mainly nocturnal and prefers hunting on the ground, though it climbs well and often rests on the limb of a tree during the day. It is not so fond of water and will use bridges rather than swim. Its tracks are like those of a big house cat, about two inches square, and are laid almost in a straight line. The walking stride is about ten inches but when trotting extends up to thirteen inches. A bobcat will wade up to its belly in snow. The trail itself, unlike the straight course of the coyote, zigzags and crisscrosses all over the area as the animal explores anything that takes its curious fancy, using both sight and scent. In its new role as a commensal of man it is attracted to rubbish dumps. Its range or territory varies from four or five to ten or even fifteen square miles, according to the prey available; within it a bobcat may wander two to seven miles in a night, though the distance in a straight line will be half or less. It has regular clawing trees within the home range.

The bobcat hunts after the fashion of the family — a watch and a stalk leading up to a final spring of as much as ten feet. If it misses the first time, it gives up the chase after a few bounds. Sometimes it pounces on a sleeping victim. If possible prey approaches, it flattens itself, then rushes forward, like the leopard stalking the wild pigs (see p. 65). It also lies in ambush — a tame bobcat surprised its owners' guests by dropping on them from a doorway.

While rabbits and hares Lagomorpha are the bobcat's favorite prey in the north, an analysis of more than 200 stomach contents in the semi-arid part of California showed that rodents accounted for 60 per cent of the total diet, lagomorphs only 30 per cent, with a few birds thrown in. Squirrels and chipmunks are hunted in the woods, and the noisy young of flickers in their tree-hole nests are marked down and raided. The bobcat also takes porcupines and is apparently able to pass their quills through its intestines without mishap. It can kill a fawn easily and in winter occasionally attacks adult deer, jumping on them as a lynx does. One had a battle with a buck for several hours until they were disturbed, and a twenty-pound bobcat is credited with bringing down an animal weighing 200 pounds. However, big game is eaten as carrion. Like all cats, it will prey on livestock from chickens and turkeys to sheep and calves. When times are hard it hunts frogs and fish. The kill is often covered after the first feed, ready for a second visit.

Apart from man and his dogs, the bobcat has few serious enemies. Horned owls will buzz it, pumas occasionally attack and eat it, and it gets chased by deer, especially does with fawns. It runs from dogs, but several are needed to master it, and it fights like a fury when cornered. Often, however, it doubles like a rabbit and is difficult to bring to bay. Mexicans eat its flesh, but the fur is considered brittle and is not of much value.

The bobcat is usually silent, except when fighting for its life, or at mating time from January to March. Then males may travel up to twenty miles in search of a mate to serenade with an unexpected repertoire. They are promiscuous and form no lasting union. After a gestation period of about ten weeks, one to four (usually two or three) kittens are born in a den on a rocky ledge or in a tree hole. The breeding season may be later in the south — or there may be a second litter — because young have been seen in October in Mexico. They are spotted at birth and weigh about twelve ounces; their eyes open after nine or ten days. Spring litters are weaned in June and become independent in early autumn when they weigh five or six pounds each. Families often stay together for the winter. Otherwise the bobcat hunts alone, breeding when one year old. In captivity one has lived for fifteen years, but the expectation of life in the wild must be much less.

Because it is less dependent on a single main prey animal, the numbers of the bobcat do not fluctuate as do those of the lynx, and with the emergence of more enlightened ideas on conservation, its part as a useful control on rodents is gradually being recognized.

THE LYNX (Plate 33)

The Canada or northern lynx is, as we have already seen, a geographical race of a species found all round the world in what is called the Holarctic region. In terms of continents, therefore, it is the most widely distributed of all the cats. It has special adaptations: thick fur and the big paws that act like snowshoes. But it is not much bigger than a bobcat; in fact, its range of measurements compares with that of the more southerly animal. The total length runs from just under three feet to four feet, males being rather larger than females. They stand twenty-two to twenty-four inches at the shoulder, and the weight range is twelve to twenty-five pounds, exceptional animals going to forty pounds — heavier than any bobcat.

The coat, much sought after as fur, is a mixture of tawny yellow, dark brown, and black, with a beautiful frosted appearance due to the fact that part of the long guard hairs are silvery white. The underparts are cinnamon-colored, shading to white on the cheek ruff, which is crossed with black stripes. The long buff-brown ears have white spots and slender black tufts. Unlike the bobcat's, the tip of the tail is entirely black, though higher up the underside is white. The pads become even more hairy in winter and leave indistinct marks that can be confused with those of a puma. A rare blue "dilute" form occurs about once in a thousand skins. Lynx flesh is said to be remarkably white and tender and is often eaten by trappers and Indians.

Once the range of *Felis lynx* extended to Pennsylvania and Indiana; it is still to be found in northern New England, the Adirondack Mountains of New York State, and on the U.S. side of the Great Lakes, but only a few hundred skins come each year from south of the Canadian border. The lynx is still common in Alaska. A favorite habitat is the northern fir forest with its swamps or muskegs, but when food is scarce it hunts out over the open tundra. Like the bobcat it is nocturnal and may zigzag or wander in wide circles when searching for game. Normally it walks but can gallop for short distances. It can climb but prefers to hunt on the ground, where its special prey the snowshoe rabbit lives; it swims well, sometimes low in the water, sometimes with back raised, and has been known to cover two miles at a go. When near the end of a stalk, the lynx stretches out to peer over a rocky ledge, then makes a final spring, landing on the victim's back with feet together and crushing it by the impact, before biting through neck or brain.

Charles Sheldon described how one dropped onto a two-year-old Dall ram, a forefoot on each side of the neck, and tried to bite the left eye. Falling at times, the ram struggled on through the snow for a hundred yards, then sank down exhausted. Sheldon shot the lynx, which had changed its attack and bitten out the right eye; he thought the eyes were chosen as the most vulnerable part of the thick-coated ram. When deer are attacked, the jugular vein is the target.

Other prey includes lemmings, mice, squirrels, skunks, and even foxes, also ground-living game birds. The lynx has a sensitive nose. It will dig up carrion though it much prefers fresh meat, "hot and quivering" as Victor Cahalane puts it. It takes fish but only when other food is scarce.

Like the bobcat, the lynx is a silent animal, occasionally miaowing when on the hunt. But at mating time the males, to quote Cahalane's racy account once more, "may loose a series of yells that compensate for a whole year of silence . . . their passionate cries to the females have different arias but do not diminish in volume."

After this vociferous courtship and mating have been consummated, the female has a gestation period of about two months before bearing a litter of one to five, usually three, in the customary well-hidden feline den: in rocks, a hollow log, or a dense windfall of timber. At first the babies are not much bigger than house kittens and are reddish brown, decorated with stripes and spots. Their eyes open fully after ten days and they remain close to the den for the first two months. At four months they resemble small adults and have been eating meat for some time. The family stays together for the first winter and has been seen hunting in line; parties of six to eleven lynxes recorded were perhaps a union of families in severe weather. The lynx is mature when one year old and may live to be ten or twelve in captivity.

Few natural enemies trouble it, though it has been known to fly from a wolverine. It is easily trapped, and it is from annual trapping returns that Charles Elton worked out the classic relationship between a predator and its prey. As early as 1907 Sheldon had observed on Mount McKinley in Alaska that most lynxes would rather starve than change to other foods when snowshoe rabbits became scarce, though one female who switched her diet remained fat. Elton found that the number of pelts sold each year varied enormously, from about 2000 to 36,000, and that the peak numbers were on an average of 9·6 years apart. Peaks did not occur all over Canada at the same time, but in each area the interval between them was much the same. The fluctuations of the lynx pelts — and hence of the population as a whole — followed fluctuations in the numbers of snowshoe rabbits, their favorite food. When the snowshoe "crashes" every seven to ten years, the lynxes are doomed. These curious cycles are a feature of northern latitudes, perhaps because they are inhabited by few kinds of animals and each predator has really only one prey. They are a lesson to us about relying too much on monocultures.

7. The Cats of Europe

ALTHOUGH TO A CHINESE or an Egyptian its civilization may seem par-
venu, the impact of man on the wildlife of Europe during the past few
centuries has been far heavier than that of more ancient cultures. Nowhere,
of course, is this more true than in my native Belgium, but Britain, my
first adopted home, runs it close. So I think it is rather remarkable that a
genuinely native wild member of the cat family survives there and is, if
anything, improving its position.

THE EUROPEAN WILDCAT (Scottish form shown on Plates 4, 35)

For the first of Europe's few cats, then, let us look at what has been named
Felis silvestris grampia, the last name a tribute to the Grampian Mountains,
that elusive range whose exact site baffled the Roman invaders and still
baffles the modern tourists. At one time, just before the First World War,
the Scottish wildcat had been driven out of the central Highlands — where
most maps hopefully locate the Grampians — into the remotest districts of
the northwest. Professor James Ritchie, one of the pioneers of British nature
conservation, was gloomy about the future of the wildcat when he wrote his
classic book on the animal life of Scotland in 1920; but already the war
years — when gamekeepers were occupied with more dangerous enemies —
had turned the tide slightly in its favor. By 1926 J. G. Millais, the great
animal painter, was able to report in *The Times* of London that one had
been trapped on the edge of the Highlands only a few miles from Perth.
He did not attribute the southward spread to the war, and gave evidence
that it had begun about 1910 and was at least partly due to an enlightened
landowner in Inverness-shire, whose keepers had orders not to destroy wildcats. One of them actually released a lightly trapped male, which may have
become a progenitor of the new Grampian stock.

Twenty years later, after another world war, Sir William Taylor conducted a survey through the staff of the Forestry Commission, now the most important landowner in the Highlands, controlling vast acreages where most wild animals find sanctuary. Wildcats were reported from forty-five out of eighty forest areas on the mainland of northern Scotland and were said to be resident in twenty-four and "occasional" in twenty-one of these. The foresters were also asked their opinion of the animal's progress. In twelve areas it was thought to be increasing, in ten to be decreasing, and in the remaining twenty-three to be static. Nowhere had it penetrated lowland Scotland, nor was it recorded from Sutherland, a former stronghold. However, there are very few state forests in that bleak county. The latest survey, conducted by Dr. David Jenkins of Aberdeen University, shows a decrease in the northwest, probably due to the local effect of myxomatosis, but this is balanced by an increase in the eastern Highlands, where there are plenty of mountain hares and grouse. In the county of Angus, about one hundred were killed annually in the 1940's and 1950's in parts of two glens alone; and they have at last broken out of the Highlands and been seen within forty miles of Edinburgh.

To summarize Jenkins' figures, wildcats were reported to be present or formerly present on 100 out of 135 estates and forests in eleven counties. Forty-four areas reported increases, twenty-one decreases, and thirty-five "no change" or "no opinion." Some of these estimates were backed by figures and the survey must be one of the most accurate yet made for a member of the Felidae. Dr. Jenkins concludes that the wildcat is probably more abundant in Scotland now than at any time in human memory.

Over the rest of Britain the extermination of genuine wildcats was probably accomplished by 1850, except perhaps in Wales. Colin Matheson of the National Museum in Cardiff measured the leg bones of a cat from Pembrokeshire; they were as long as those of a Scottish wildcat and considerably longer than those of house cats. He thought it possible that a "wild cat strain" lingered among the feral cats in some parts of Wales, thus raising a point which affects many of the smaller kinds of cat the world over.

To what extent do "wild" cats interbreed with house cats? In previous chapters I have several times mentioned crosses, for example with the black-footed cat and jungle cat. Well, we might go back a stage and ask whether the wild kinds hybridize with each other, because it is pretty clear that the European wildcat, the African wildcat (*Felis libyca*), the jungle cat (*F. chaus*), and probably the black-footed cat are very closely related. One modern authority, for example, believes that the cats still holding out in the Mediterranean islands — Corsica, Sardinia, and Majorca — belong to the European species and not to the African, as is generally accepted.

We also believe that the house cat, though it has been given the rank of a species in its own right since the days of Linnaeus, is descended from the African cat, perhaps crossed with the European cat at some stage. On the face of it, therefore, there seems no reason why these small cats should not hybridize with each other and with house cats when the opportunity occurs. Most writers accept that this is true of Scottish wildcats and consider that dilution of the wild stock by crossbreeding is now a far more serious threat than the old enemy man, though, of course, he is indirectly responsible, just as he is responsible for contaminating the pure breed of wild doves with escaped racing pigeons, and the remaining British polecats with polecat-ferrets. David Stephen, who knows the wildlife of the Highlands well, says that the mating is always supposed to be between a wild tom and a feral or domestic female and quotes the case of a deer-stalker who raised the tempestuous offspring of such a union. These hybrids can be told from pure wildcats by their pointed tails and sometimes by smaller size.

House cats have been going feral in Scotland for many years, so we might expect that by now domestic color patterns would be widespread among the crossbred population, as has happened with the rock doves. In fact, the striped tabby pattern still seems universal. I am no geneticist, but from what I understand of the most interesting work of Dr. A. G. Searle on the coat colors of house cats, it seems that the ancestral tabby is dominant to black, the most popular domestic color — selected, of course, because black cats are "lucky" (in some countries and regions) — and probably to most other varieties. Therefore the first generation of hybrids between wild tabbies and house cats of any color is likely also to be tabby, and if varieties appear in subsequent generations they would be at a disadvantage against their tabby litter-mates, or might even be deliberately eliminated by the parents.

We might ask, of course, who has ever seen the principals of one of these mixed marriages together? This is not a very fair question, because the union is likely to be nocturnal and brief. Miss Frances Pitt proved years ago that hybrids between wild cats and house cats were fertile, so there is no reason why dilution should not occur.

After this digression let us get back to *grampia* itself. I have already said that it bears the striped tabby pattern, as distinct from the blotched tabby, which Dr. Searle thinks has arisen by mutation since the house cat became domesticated. Within this general pattern, nevertheless, there is a good deal of variation. This is said to show the influence of house cats, but it is not really as great as in many of the other species we have met. Well-grown wildcats are about two feet long from nosetip to the base of the thickly furred tail, which may be a foot long and ends in a characteristic rounded black tip. The head appears bigger and flatter than a house cat's and the legs are definitely longer, the thighbone averaging nearly an inch more. Dr. Jenkins says the horn color of the claws is a good distinguishing character. Males are on the whole bigger than females, though their weights overlap, toms running from a minimum of six and one-half to more than fifteen pounds and females from seven to ten pounds; the record Scottish specimen scaled fifteen pounds ten ounces.

So much for statistics. What does this famous animal, the fiercest carnivore left in Britain, look like? How does it behave in its fleeting contacts with man? Thomas Pennant in 1776 called it the "British tiger"; Charles St. John, who restlessly hunted so many fine birds and mammals to their deaths, almost fell on top of one when fishing in Sutherland: "I was quite as much startled as the animal herself could be, when I saw the wild-looking beast so unexpectedly rush out from between my feet, with every hair on her body standing on end, making her look twice as large as she really was." His terriers cornered her, but as St. John closed in she sprang straight at his face over the dogs' heads. He went for her with an improvised club, remarking, rather like Walter Elliot and the tiger, "I never saw an animal fight so desperately, or one which was so difficult to kill. If a tame cat has nine lives, a wild cat must have a dozen."

Today admiration is no longer just a form of obituary. David Stephen writes of "a cateran of fire and brimstone, implacably savage, reputedly untameable" but his theme has a basis of live and let live, though he admits that some of his best views of wildcats have been when dogs have bolted them and they turned at bay. I asked Bruce Campbell, Editor of this World Wildlife Series, how often, in hours of boyhood walking over the hills of North Argyll (a good country for them), he had come across a wildcat. His first meeting was one evening in March when he was half hidden under a rock in the dry course of a hill burn. Suddenly he was aware of a large tabby cat coming down from boulder to boulder. He must have moved slightly because the animal stopped, looked at him, and then just wasn't there anymore. He had never seen anything travel so quickly. But, he told me, "brief as the encounter was, the large rather flattened head and long legs stand out in my memory — it was quite unlike a domestic cat." His only other sighting was one glorious August afternoon, on a basalt hillside alive with rabbits. A friend, on a first visit to Scotland, said, "There's something like a cat" — it had a full, bushy tail and was running along a narrow track among a party of sheep, which for a few moments blocked it path. "It paused and glared up at us before leaving the track and running up the steep slope. As we saw three golden eagles and at least fifty red deer that day, my friend got a somewhat heightened impression of Highland wild life; I hardly liked to tell him it was only the second time I had ever met a wild cat!"

The nocturnal habits of the Scottish wildcat are responsible for this lack of firsthand observation. David Jenkins says it has seldom been watched for more than a minute or two, though its present habitat extends from moorland and woodland to cultivated valleys and it often visits farms and other habitations, even leaving its paw marks on windowsills. In fact, most wildcats probably live below the thousand-foot contour line, though they may be seen at twice that height.

The usual evidence of a wildcat is the track of paw marks, typically in a straight line, in snow or mud, or the black droppings which it usually leaves exposed. It may travel several miles in a night and has been traced from rabbit hole to rabbit hole, which suggests that it may have a regular beat. Most writers agree that its chief prey is now the rabbit, which in spite of myxomatosis is still common in parts of the Highlands. Before the introduction of the rabbit in the Middle Ages it must have hunted mainly the mountain or blue hare. J. G. Millais recounted the story of James Geddes, of Ardverikie in Inverness-shire, who saw a hare run up an estate road with a cat in full cry after it. He stood aside and both animals passed him within a yard as they dashed into a small quarry, where the cat killed the hare by jumping on its back and giving it a bite in the neck — typical feline tactics. The cat stayed by its victim until Geddes was almost upon it, when "it sprang sullenly out of the way. Geddes had the hare for dinner and said wildcats are 'guid bastes that should be in swarms.' "

The killing of grouse and other game birds has been made the excuse for exterminating wildcats on shooting estates; they also take lambs which makes them unpopular with shepherds. They hunt small rodents and birds, eating them whole, and David Stephen has seen one stalk and seize a squirrel. He knows it can kill a roe deer fawn and thinks it could manage a weakly red deer calf; he has seen hinds react strongly to a cat. Even after it had gone they "milled around, stamping, with their ears up, obviously unsettled." Fish seem to be unusual food, though Stephen has a record of a cat drowned with some in a fish trap.

David Jenkins describes a feeding routine with larger prey, such as we have met with other cats. The head may be torn off, the brains and tongue eaten, and perhaps some of the choicer entrails. The flight feathers of game birds may be bitten off before eating, and a kill, if not consumed at one meal, may be buried, and it is usually removed to cover if made in daytime. Wildcats do not "play" with their prey in the way that house cats do, thus shocking sensitive owners, but they may kill and leave small animals like shrews which are unpalatable.

As with other cats, the mating season is announced with unearthly cater-wauling. St. John did not "know a more harsh and unpleasant cry than that of the wild cat, or one more likely to be the origin of superstitious fears." This happens twice a year, in March and again at the end of May or early in June, the litters being born in May and August after about two months' gestation. Dr. Jenkins has some evidence of a third litter in parts of Scotland. This multiple breeding season is considered to be strong evidence for the dilution of the Scottish stock by house cats, because the wildcat in continental Europe only breeds once a year. But, as David Stephen points out, if dilution has taken place, why not also on the Continent? Bruce Campbell tells me that many birds are single- or double-brooded in different parts of their range. The kittens are born in darkness, often in one of those great cairns, or heaps of boulders, which may also shelter foxes, badgers, and their prey of rabbits and mice. Two to four is the usual litter size, and it is generally said that, once their eyes are open, the babies are untamable, even if born in captivity. David Stephen succeeded in taming one, but it took him seven weeks and several cuts. The kittens come out of the den when a month old, begin hunting at three months, and are weaned at four. They are mature when a year old.

Outside Britain the wildcat is still widely distributed across Europe and into western Asia, though it does not inhabit Scandinavia. It is typically a forest animal, but of more southern range than the lynx. Theodor Haltenorth, A. de Leuw, and other German naturalists have studied its habits carefully, and it appears to be more diurnal than the Scottish wildcat — especially in summer and autumn, when it is hunting hard to stoke up for the lean days of winter. Probably because of a higher population, German wildcats may be confined to quite small territories of about one hundred and fifty acres, which the males defend after marking boundary trees with their claws, by urinating, or by rubbing their hindquarters against them, evidently to release the secretion of the anal gland. Analysis of their food in Germany shows that 65 per cent consists of mice and voles and only 8 per cent of game birds. They are now protected.

THE AFRICAN WILDCAT (Plate 11)

In a remote village, Professor M. F. M. Meiklejohn was shown a tame individual of the Sardinian wildcat and said it looked quite different from a house cat, but nothing seems to be known of the habits of these Mediterranean island races of *Felis libyca*.

THE LYNX (Plate 34)

So there is really only one more species of importance in Europe, the lynx, which we have already met briefly in Asia and more fully in America. It can be claimed as a former British mammal on the strength of bones from several sites in England, Wales, and Scotland, but there is no evidence that it survived into historic times. Dr. Kai Curry-Lindahl, Swedish zoologist and conservationist, has studied the changes in its distribution.

Since 1800 it has vanished from the Alps and their foothills. A few remain in the Balkans and Carpathians, and thence northward in pockets to the Scandinavian forests, its chief stronghold in western Europe.

Dr. Curry-Lindahl tells me that a drastic decline took place in Sweden during the second half of the last century, due to direct persecution by man. The southern limit of its range moved from the 56th to the 62nd parallel of latitude, and by 1925 the lynx was restricted to a small area in the center of the country and was very near extinction. It was given total legal protection in 1928 and a slow recovery began. During the 1940's it reappeared in its old haunts in the southwest and the south, where it still occurs, though the closed season was reduced to ten months in 1943. A census in 1950 recorded 175 lynxes, 152 of them in the north. A separate estimate the same year for Swedish Lapland gave fifty-three animals, which had increased to 127 in 1957. In 1963 the population for the whole country was between 200 and 300. Local populations also survive in southern and central Norway, and one lynx has recently been killed in Denmark, after several hundred years' absence.

Far from the forests of northern and eastern Europe, a small population of lynxes holds on in Spain — a few still in the Pyrenees, but mainly in very different terrain, in Portugal and in the Coto Doñana beside the Guadalquivir. Part of that wonderful Coto Doñana area has now been saved by the action of the Spanish Government and the resources of the World Wildlife Fund, coming not a moment too soon as the hand of the "developer" overshadowed the dunes and the marismas, the lagoons and the pinewoods.

Here lynxes of the Spanish race, which several authorities regard as a distinct species (*Felis pardina*), have been protected for some years by enlightened landowners like the González family, and here Dr. Antonio Valverde Gómez studied them a few years ago with the assistance of several observant gamekeepers. These men, like their counterparts who watched the leopards in Ceylon (pp. 64–65), are able because of their long hours in the field to see things that no sportsman or casual visitor has a hope of observing. Even Valverde did not see an adult lynx except in captivity, but he was shown dens, tracks, and other evidence and was able to build up a picture of the animal's life and habits such as we have for few others of the smaller cats.

Not that Spanish lynxes are so small. A male killed when at its fattest in December weighed nearly sixty pounds and a nursing female in June was only a pound or so lighter. The keepers maintain that the male is always paler and larger, particularly about the head, neck, and whiskers, and that he makes bigger pugmarks.

Valverde considers that the specialized habitat is the chief distinction of the Spanish race of lynxes. They are not forest animals like the northern races but live either in the rather open woods of pines, pistachio scrub, and junipers which cover parts of the great dunes, or in the belt dominated by *jaguarzo* (*Halimium*) a pale-foliaged shrub with striking yellow flowers. This lies between the woods and the open marshes, or marismas, and is studded with old cork oaks and interspersed with stretches of heath, bracken, and grassland and by dense thickets of brambles, broom, and gorse which are almost impenetrable for man and make splendid hideouts for the lynxes. In general this habitat is like that occupied by the caracal in North Africa, and Valverde, who has studied its Moroccan haunts, believes that the two species replace each other geographically. So I am quite right when I speak of the caracal as the African lynx. I suppose the position is very roughly the same as between the Canada lynx and bobcat in North America, where the bobcat prefers open to dense woodland and extends into the deserts of the southwestern states and Mexico.

While night is the most active time for the Spanish lynx, it is often about by day and seems curiously indifferent to man. The gamekeepers of the Coto sometimes see one in broad daylight ambling along one of its favorite paths — it occasionally trots but will only run when chased — or, when standing still and almost hidden in the scrub, they have watched one approach and even sit down to have a better look at the queer object before quietly taking itself off. One keeper stalked a lynx by its trail and found it asleep in the sun in a clearing among the pistachios, close to its latrine, a pile of feces nine inches high. But this disturbance of its privacy was too much for the animal and it did not come back again.

The Spanish lynx hunts like its northern relatives (and most other cats, for that matter). It uses all available cover, and when that gives out it crawls flat on the ground until close enough for a spring. If it misses (which is not often) it does not give chase. A favorite method of the lynx when after rabbits is to stalk silently to the edge of a clearing where they are feeding and then wait for one to come within range. When attacking young deer, it leaps at the throat if the fawn is standing or jumps onto its neck if it is lying down. One keeper saw a lynx astride a red deer calf that was shrieking in its terror. Occasionally a pair hunt together; a keeper in Andalusia surprised one mauling a kid while another stood by. He shot both of them in understandable anger, but in such fashion the lynx has been exterminated throughout most of Spain.

Like the caracal, the lynx hunts game birds, chiefly the red-legged partridge. A covey flew over one that was near its drinking place. It jumped up and seized a bird in the air with its claws, then carried it off in its mouth. Apparently the prey is always taken away from the killing point. If it is small enough, it is held with the captor's head high, the tail also jauntily vertical and switching from side to side. Heavier loads are dragged: a red deer calf was moved about one hundred and fifty yards and a rabbit with its trap — lynxes often poach along trap and snare lines — over half a mile.

The Spanish lynx only eats part of its victims. In spite of the flesh on them, the legs as well as the back and entrails of a rabbit are usually left; the head, neck, breast, legs, and wing muscles of a partridge are eaten, but the lynx only samples the shoulder and neck, or perhaps a bit of the hindquarters, of a deer. After its meal it covers the rest of the kill with sand and litter, making a characteristic mound nearly a foot high, from which the legs sometimes protrude pathetically. Despite these preparations the lynx does not come again — unlike most of its relatives, including the wildcats, which are also found in the Coto. In fact, it does not eat carrion at all and foxes often profit by its leavings.

There is no doubt that the common European rabbit, which often swarms in the grassy areas, is its main prey; but the Spanish lynx is not dependent on rabbits as is the Canada lynx on the snowshoe rabbit. There are several alternatives which I have already mentioned: young of both red and fallow deer, at their most vulnerable when the female lynxes have litters to feed, red-legged partridges, and perhaps other birds. The hare (*Lepus capensis*) is rare in the Coto and seldom hunted. Although sheep and goats are occasionally killed, the lynx has no reputation as a pest of livestock — in fact it shuns the few habitations of the area. Reptiles and large insects abound, but there are no records of its eating them.

Apart from man, the Spanish lynx has few enemies. There are several smaller competitors with which it sometimes clashes. Keepers have found buried foxes, terribly wounded at the neck but not eaten. One actually saw a fox baiting a lynx, jumping away every time its foe was provoked to attack. Small dogs and the wild mongooses are sometimes attacked: a terrific fight between a lynx and a big mongoose ended in the latter's death. There is some evidence that the lynx occasionally falls foul of an otter; but, as Valverde points out, these fights are not systematic; they are incidental to the common interest of all these carnivores, except the otter, in the rabbits.

Man shoots the lynx in drives and some are caught in traps. The annual mortality from these causes in the Coto may be fifteen to twenty. During shoots lynxes take to the thickest cover or climb trees but occasionally break out ahead of the game and give the hunter easy opportunities. There is an old record of one severely wounding a keeper and then escaping. Since the poor animal had been shot, taken for dead, and carried over the man's shoulders to his home, its reaction when it recovered its senses is not surprising.

The main mating time, Valverde thinks, is in January and lasts about a month, followed by a gestation period of about two months. Judging from the size of kittens seen in the spring, it would appear that courting may begin as early as November. Only love makes the lynx exchange its normal silence for a raucous miaowing heard mainly at dusk or in the night. A male watched by a keeper called as it walked, neither raising nor lowering its head, and pausing from time to time. Valverde suggests that male and female answer each other, but I wonder whether rival males are not involved in these duets; he says nothing about the fights in which other cats indulge.

The kittens may be born in a variety of situations. In the jaguarzal country dense thickets are the preferred site, followed by holes in old oaks, perhaps ten feet high. The vegetation round about is used for the nest; no hair is added and the site is kept beautifully clean, at least while the kittens are small. In the pinewoods Valverde recorded dens most frequently in pistachio scrub, but two were up to forty feet in the old nests of white storks in pines, two others were down burrows, and one in thick junipers. Seven out of fourteen litters had two kittens, four were of three, two of four, and one had a single baby; as far as he could tell, the sexes were evenly divided at birth. When born, the kittens are no bigger than rats and often seem to grow at different rates. Probably the smaller ones die off. But one keeper saw a litter of three or four playing in the morning sunshine when they were big enough to run up and down the pines with remarkable agility. At about four months of age they leave the area of the den, and become independent a month or so later. We do not know whether the father ever helps with family duties.

When it has grown up, each lynx establishes itself in a sort of territory which includes a principal den or lair and a hunting area often where jaguarzal, grassland, and bracken ground meet and which it visits by several tracks. The territory in summer has a diameter of from two and one-half to six and one-half miles but may have to be extended in winter when game is scarce. One lynx was tracked for up to twenty miles in a district where it was the only one of its kind.

The future of the Spanish lynx lies under two threats: the possible disappearance of its principal prey through myxomatosis, and the direct or indirect effect of man and his works. The saving of the best part of the Coto Doñana may have come just in time to save also one of its most exciting inhabitants.

Apart from such leopards as still survive in the mountain forests of southeastern Russia, we have come to the end of the existing cats of Europe. But we must at least pay our respects to the lion, which can also be claimed as a British mammal within the period of human occupation. In Greece, where the Thracian lion was famous, it was known to Aristotle and to the Roman historian Pliny, though it was probably nearly extinct in his day, the first century A.D. Dr. Guggisberg believes there were two species, the cave lion, without a mane or tail-tuft, and the present-day lion, existing side by side for a time. After the cave lion died out, he thinks — as I mentioned in Chapter 3 — that the smaller species retreated south because of the afforestation of Europe rather than suffering extermination at the hands of primitive man. It found suitable open habitats in Greece and lingered there until perhaps the remnant was captured and "butchered to make a Roman holiday."

8. Cats and Men

THE CHARACTER who to millions is the most important member of the family makes his (or should I write "her" — some people regard all cats as feminine) main appearance late in this book, though I have constantly referred to him in earlier chapters. The house cat (Plate 36), a species in its own right, is one of the most widespread pets in the world, counted in tens of millions both in Europe and North America, with a feral population more numerous than that of any wild relative and exerting a profound influence on the wildlife around it, especially on islands.

The passion for documentation is a characteristic of modern man. Whoever first domesticated the cat left us no records and I believe its origins will never be definitely traced. Since house cats seem to have appeared first in ancient Egypt, it is generally held that the African wildcat is the main ancestor of the synthetic animal we know today. It is also possible that the jungle cat was tamed long ago in India. And how do we know that the early cats of Etruria were not descended from the European wildcat? And what happened in China and other countries of eastern Asia?

At all events we now have a creature of enormously variable appearance, like most other domestic animals, but with enough basic characters to permit us to describe it as I have described its relations. A full-grown male weighs from nine to seventeen pounds, with the occasional giant going up to twenty-eight pounds; females are lighter, averaging six to ten pounds. The combined head and body length is about two feet, with the tail — except in the Manx breed — adding up to a foot more. House cats stand eight to ten inches at the shoulder. Toms mature when between nine months and a year; females may be able to breed at six months but usually do not have their first litters until they are a year old. Gestation lasts about eight weeks and litters range from four or five to as many as nine kittens in some breeds. Most are born in spring, from February to May, but a cat can easily have two or three litters a year and breed up to the age of fourteen, exceptionally when nearly twice as old. A cat may live to be as much as thirty years old, as long as, or longer than, its bigger relatives. This is partly due to its sheltered life.

As everyone knows, kittens are born blind but furry, weighing only a few ounces. Their eyes open to the darkness of their "den" — it may be a basket hidden behind a chair or in a cupboard — after about ten days; they grow rapidly and start to explore the outside world after three weeks, when you can begin to wean them. Their mother also begins to house-train them if provided with a tray nearby. At two months they should be more or less independent of her. Domestic toms are usually no more friendly to their progeny than wild ones and will eat them if they get the chance.

The playfulness of kittens is proverbial, but it is, of course, a form of training for life; the house cat remains in part a wild animal, earning a good share of its keep by hunting just like the rest of the family. A cat living in the country in Britain may take a dozen different kinds of small mammals, from a pygmy shrew up to a leveret or young hare in size, and with a vertical range from moles to bats, though I do not think it will often try conclusions with a hedgehog.

A friend has told me how he was awakened in the night by a frightening growl, switched on the light and found his cat standing over a warm, quivering, long-eared bat which must have flown into the bedroom. This cat also knocked down swallows when they flew low, as others have caught kingfishers by lying on top of a streambank. Bird killing, of course, gets cats a bad name, though some owners claim to be able to cure it. A bell on a collar is one method, if you don't mind the cat's developing a frustration neurosis as a result. Some cats learn to scoop fish out of shallow water, but more serious, especially on islands, is their fondness for catching lizards: the survival of the green and wall lizards of Jersey, for example, is said to be threatened by marauding pussies; the depredations of house cats gone feral are even worse, and find their place in the next chapter.

I had myself, when I lived some miles out of Rochester, New York, a cat that was an inveterate hunter — or, rather, I should say an inveterate collector, because it captured its victims and proudly brought them home to drop them at my feet on the living room floor not only alive but usually quite uninjured. I was collecting and breeding small mammals at the time, and owed many unusual specimens — starnose mole, voles, jumping mice — to this efficient cat. It also brought in frogs, lizards, and snakes, the latter very much irritated, as is perhaps natural. Its proudest achievement was the dragging in of a hare, larger than itself, with a broken leg, and of a full-grown pheasant apparently in perfectly sound condition which had no difficulty leaving my living room under its own power the moment the cat released it.

It is as hunters of rats and mice in the granaries of Egypt three thousand years ago that cats first came into close association with man and attained divinity. The goddess Pasht, or Bubastis, is shown as a woman with a cat's head. In the time of Thothmes IV, about 1500 B.C., a temple at Beni-Hausan was dedicated to her; behind it was a pit for mummified cats which were sent there for burial from all over Egypt. Cats themselves shared the sanctity of their patroness: in a fire they were rescued before the human occupants, and when one died all members of the household shaved off their eyebrows as a sign of mourning. So strong was the tradition that a Roman soldier who accidentally killed a cat was himself executed though he belonged to an occupying army, and no doubt protested vigorously.

Many models of these slim, striped Egyptian cats have come down to us, made of precious stones and wood. They wore earrings and necklaces; and children's necklaces and bracelets were made of repeated small cat figures. A model cat that was evidently a birthday present to a little girl from her pet has been preserved. Cats also appear as part of the motif in ornamentation of all kinds. Outside Egypt, we find cats mentioned in Indian writings about the time of Christ; the Chinese philosopher Confucius, who lived about 500 B.C., had a tame cat. It is more surprising that Freya, whose name we use every Friday, is shown in a chariot pulled by two cats, suggesting that even in then remote Scandinavia, where wildcats do not occur, these animals were well known.

From Egypt cats were introduced to Greece and Italy, though the Etruscans also had them, perhaps independently, in their mysterious civilization. When Europe was submerged in the Dark Ages, cats appeared in the East; about A.D. 600 Mohammed is supposed to have preached holding one in his arms, and cats guarded the sacred manuscripts in Japanese temples.

House cats were rare in early Britain, but some evidently survived the departure of the legions because the Welsh prince Hywel the Good, whose famous ordinances made about A.D. 948 have come down to us, fixed the price of a newborn kitten at a penny, rising to twopence after its first successful mouse hunt; and there were stiff fines for stealing or killing a cat from his granary. About the same time Henry the Fowler, the German king, imposed a heavy fine for "caticide." In legend and story too, as the tales of Puss in Boots and Dick Whittington show, the cat was highly thought of as guide and counselor.

Gradually poor puss came down in the world through his association with old women who were branded as witches, and during the age of witch hunts cats were regarded as familiars and were burned with their mistresses. Yet, by a curious twist, the black cat, most feared of all, turned — as cat status improved again — into the lucky black cat of some regions and today, by deliberate selection from the litter, is the most common type in southern England according to H. N. Southern, who has kindly shown me the results of his interesting field study of coat colors.

As the cat climbed back into favor, owners began to select and breed for particular colors, until today between thirty and forty breeds are recognized by British cat-fanciers and the number is continually being added to. The first cat show in England was held at the Crystal Palace, London, in 1871, and cats were shown among other pets in New York in 1884, attaining their own event in 1895. There are now cat associations in Canada, Australia, New Zealand, South Africa, and many other countries.

American fanciers organize their cats into fewer breeds than the British, according to supposed countries of origin (Siamese, Burmese, Abyssinian, Russian, and Manx) and hair length, short-haired or long-haired (derived from the mating of Persian and Angora strains) and "rex" or curly-coated cats. These last developed from a mutation that occurred about thirty years ago in Britain. The British classification is based on the long-haired and short-haired types, which are then subdivided according to coat color and eye color. While some of these color groups breed true, others have to be worked for by crossing colors and are therefore not breeds in a genetic sense. The cat population at large mixes freely, of course, and it is the resulting trends in different countries which interest Southern and Dr. A. G. Searle, who has published scientific papers on gene frequencies and variations in the cats of London and Singapore. So puss progressed from witch's familiar to biologist's guinea pig. Some popular beliefs about cat colors are true: almost all tortoiseshells are females; when a male does appear, he is sterile.

But I am afraid the Manx cat did not originate as the Island legend would have it. The story goes that the Manx warriors, envious of the plumed helmets of their Irish or Danish foes, took to killing cats and adorning themselves with the tails. At last one wise female had her litter in secrecy on top of Snaefell, the highest hill, and bit off their tails, so that they were no longer of interest to the vain Manxmen. Mother cats passed on the secret to their daughters, who continued biting off their kittens' tails until they were born without them. This classic example of belief in the inheritance of acquired characteristics must antedate Jean Lamarck by about eight hundred years, but I daresay even he found it too radical. Another version derives the tailless cat from a wrecked ship of the Armada — a favorite explanation all down the west side of the British Isles for curious human features, too.

The tailless cat, though so distinctive, is not a pure strain. Indeed, attempts to breed a pure Manx strain lead to litters that fail to survive; and in any case the kittens may be born with tails or stumps as well as none. A good Manx cat has no tail at all, a rounded rear, long back legs, and seems almost to hop like a rabbit. Yet it is no less agile than other cats. Tailless animals occur in Japan and Malaya, where there is also a variety with a kinked tail.

The proliferation of beautiful and unusual breeds shows that the cat is on top of the pet world again, with all this implies today. The cats' meat-man has been succeeded by the attractively labeled proprietary tin, on sale at the best grocers and stores; cats star in television advertisements for these products, each more nutritious than the last. Cats have invaded the picture card and Christmas card field, as they invaded the frescoes of ancient Egypt, and have followed Puss in Boots as the heroes and heroines of countless children's stories, with the smile of Lewis Carroll's Cheshire Cat behind them all. Nor are they unknown in adult literature, where I suppose Saki's Tobermory holds pride of place. This handsome animal is taught to speak English perfectly by a German professor and uses his skill to terrorize a houseparty by threatening to reveal their nocturnal activities as observed from his own rooftop prowls. Tobermory talks in cultured, sophisticated terms. I notice that most literary cats are presented in this style, in contrast to the simple devoted dog.

But to honor all the cats immortalized by authors and famous men — though Napoleon detested them; perhaps he was too feline himself — would fill a book; so would a chronicle of their authenticated doings in real life. They form extraordinary friendships with their enemies on either side, suckling bereaved puppies and abandoned baby rabbits. They home when removed, though not so remarkably as dogs; they survive terrible disasters and injuries; they seem to know when portentous events occur. No wonder they were welcomed in eastern temples. Indeed, when I was in Siam, I could only suppose that all the blue-eyed beauties were in retreat, for I never saw any outside.

In fact, a prolonged search of several weeks in Siam and in Burma failed to reveal a single specimen which would resemble the cats we call Siamese or Burmese. Asian cats are, however, generally very different from European cats. They are gaunt and slinky, long-legged and kinky-tailed — or their tails may end in a knob; their heads are elongated, their ears long and pointed, and their eyes slanted in typically oriental style. Ship's cats are often Asian cats. They walk calmly on board at Hong Kong, Singapore, or Yokohama and make themselves at home. I have brought back several cats from Asian journeys, one of them a short-haired blue-gray tom, bought for a dollar in Lashio, on the Chinese-Burmese border, from a Chinese house of ill fame. It traveled with us on the Burma Road and later was carried from India over the mountains to Katmandu in Nepal.

I now leave the house cat, at once wild and tame, aloof and affectionate, tyrannical and pitiful, dignified and appealing — man's friend and ally on his own terms. Several other members of the Felidae, as I have already mentioned, have long associations with man. The lion, of course, heads the list. Dr. Guggisberg's book has a fascinating chapter on "The Lion in Art," tracing representations of it from the cave of Labastide in the Pyrenees, where the men of 20,000 years ago depicted the game with which Europe then teemed, to the action painters of today. He quotes the famous description of the discovery by Norbert Casteret:

. . . suddenly there appeared to my eyes the head of a roaring lion, drawn with wonderful realism. This head, more than natural size, is uncannily lifelike in its expression. There are the wrinkles around the gaping maw, fangs, eight centimetres long, protrude from the jaws, the eye is half-closed because the mouth is wide open. All this gives the brute an utterly savage appearance. The great artist who, with a pointed flint, scratched this masterpiece into the rough ceiling of the low corridor has faithfully rendered the impression of an encounter with the terrible predator!

Lion drawings are found in most of the famous French caves but are not as common as those of the animals hunted for food by paleolithic man. If, as is generally thought, these drawings were designed as a sort of sympathetic magic to attract the herds on which the artists and their companions depended, then there was not much point in drawing lions, who were uncompromising competitors. Still, there is a colored lion in Le Combel, one of the galleries at Pech-Merle, and a model of one at Isturitz.

The neolithic rock drawings of the Sahara include lions, usually as hunters themselves; but one fine lion-hunt scene dates from the comparatively recent Libyco-Berber period, which extended into the Christian era. Lion designs occur in many of the tombs of ancient Egypt, and hunting scenes were depicted on the painted chest at the entrance of the burial chamber of Tutankhamen, about 1400 B.C. At least one god and two goddesses of the Egyptian pantheon had lion heads. The sphinx of course is a lion with a human face and was adopted by several other Mediterranean peoples, including the Greeks.

The Kings of Mesopotamia are shown as lion hunters; the Hittites portrayed winged sphinxes, and by tradition Solomon's palace had lion designs. And so it is eastward into Persia and India, and even in China, where lions were never native and yet, as Dr. Guggisberg points out, seem "to have fired the Chinese imagination more than the tiger which lived in parts of their own country."

The Greeks did not use the lion extensively in their reliefs, but they adopted the sphinx extensively and added their own chimera, which breathed fire from its lion head and had a goat's body with a dragon's hindquarters. The Etruscans and Romans probably took the lion from the Greeks. It traveled back from Rome to Constantinople with the imperial games; and Ethiopia copied from Byzantium. Guggisberg describes the astonishing resemblance between a modern Abyssinian painting of the English diplomat A. W. Hodson, shown as a lion killer, and a Byzantine mosaic of the sixth century.

Medieval symbolism took up the lion from the failing Empire and often used it to represent worldly power. When heraldry came in, this aspect found expression on many a coat of arms and has echoes in the dying Lion of Lucerne, the Lion of Belfort, and the lions of Trafalgar Square. With growing interest in natural history and the opening up of Africa came the animal painters, from Joseph Wolf, who drew scenes from his mind's eye, to Kuhnert and J. G. Millais, who got their material at first hand. The tradition continues today in artists like David Shepherd, who has done such fine work on behalf of the World Wildlife Fund.

Compared to the lion, the tiger comes off rather poorly although it has inspired many eastern designs as well as superstitions. Leopards and cheetahs also occur from time to time. The latter has, of course, had a long association with man as a hunting animal, which I have already described in Chapter 5.

The cats of America have two separate traditions, that of the Indian civilizations, and that of the conquering Europeans. The puma was apparently worshiped by the ancestors of the Cochiti Indians of New Mexico and was held in reverence and respect by many other tribes; in Baja California the natives refused to interfere with it and largely subsisted on its kills. The name puma was used by some of the noble families of the Incas, rather like the lion titles of Europe. Parts of the puma were used as medicine or charms, and the European legend of the "lincurius," or precious stone, formed from the urine of a lynx was transferred by the Mexicans to the puma's excreta.

Although I have by no means exhausted the stories, legends, and symbols connected with the cat family, I think we can agree that these fierce, beautifully adapted carnivores have not been entirely at the receiving end where man is concerned and have made their mark on his culture and attitudes in almost all parts of the world.

Finally, I am indebted to Marvin L. Jones of the United States Air Force, who has made a mammals-in-captivity project his preoccupation for the past twenty years and has most kindly condensed for me the mass of information he has collected about the Felidae in the zoos of the world. I cannot do more here than summarize it still further and trust that he will eventually publish in full the fruit of these years of research. Sergeant Jones has records of thirty-two of the thirty-five wild species of cat in captivity. Not surprisingly, the three omissions are also animals of which I have been unable to find photographs: the Bornean red cat (*Felis badia*), the Chinese desert cat (*Felis bieti*), and the Andean cat (*F. jacobita*). Some of the others, for example the elusive rusty-spotted cat of Asia, have not been exhibited for many years. Twenty-three species have bred successfully in captivity, from the European wildcat, which does so with reluctance, to the lion and tiger, of which the breeding is almost an industry. On the whole animals that breed well in zoos also enjoy relatively long lives. Lions, tigers, leopards, jaguars, and pumas may all live about twenty years and occasionally longer behind bars. The snow leopard, clouded leopard, leopard cat, Temminck's cat, serval, caracal, bobcat, and cheetah are also good captives, though the cheetah has only bred in three zoos. The ocelot is now so popular as a pet in the United States that there is an owners' club.

Several cats are or have been represented by a number of geographical races in different collections. At one time Berlin specialized in this. There also has been much confusion in identifying them, and this has extended to actual species, particularly in the puzzling ocelot–margay–little spotted cat group. One zoo curator was renowned for his ability to describe a new species from a single animal!

Zoo populations can only be estimated for a few cats. Sergeant Jones believes there are at least a thousand lions and several hundred pumas in collections all over the world. There are probably thirty pairs and trios of cheetahs, about fifty individual servals, and twenty Temminck's cats; American zoos have about fifty jaguars. At the other extreme only three sand cats (*Felis margarita*) have ever been kept in European zoos, and only the London animal, whose photograph I show, lived a reasonable span.

9. The Future for Cats

THE THIRTY-FIVE WILD SPECIES of cats have inhabited all but one of the continents of the world, as we have seen, for many hundreds of thousands of years and are the survivors of a group whose first types appeared millions of years ago. How many of them will be surviving not in another hundred thousand years but in one hundred years from now? That is the terrible situation we face today — and I write "terrible" after careful thought, and not irresponsibly, because this situation involves the future of man himself.

Dr. Colin Bertram has recently told us in *Oryx* Magazine that of all the human beings who have ever lived since modern man first appeared in the world, between 3 and 4 per cent are actually alive today, and our species is increasing by a number equal to the population of Britain every four hundred days or so. What room can there be for wild animals in this human ant-heap if every ant is to be fed and clothed?

But man does not live by bread alone; he needs many other things, not all of them material — and among these are the wild animals and the wild places they live in. We who support the World Wildlife Fund and the International Union for the Conservation of Nature believe that we can continue to enjoy them if we take thought now, and act with urgency in these last few years given to us. We do not ask for vast resources: the price of a single modern weapon of war each year would supply all the money needed. But we require land, much of it useless for agriculture, and above all the help and support of men and women of good will. Shall we agree that our thirty-five cats have a place in this program of conservation and see how it stands with each of them?

The *Lion* must be first in our thoughts. He is assured of survival in zoos, and in the wild as long as the national parks and reserves of Africa are maintained; the remnant of about two hundred Indian lions should also be enough to hold out and reproduce themselves under existing protection. But, in spite of recent statements that the lion is "vermin" in parts of Africa, do not let us deceive ourselves about his chances if the reserves are breached. So we must summarize his position as safe in conserved areas only, which I shall call *Category C*.

The *Tiger* at present appears to be better off than the lion outside what I shall broadly call reserves. However, increased population and the pressure for more farmland in India, China, and Southeast Asia may soon alter this. At present we can say "safe," but the position must be kept under constant review, a classification that I call *Category B*.

Although the *Leopard* is apparently more successful than either of its bigger cousins both in Asia and Africa, a craze for leopard skins such as swept the United States in 1963 could soon wipe out this advantage. New York furriers were asking $15,000 for a Somali leopard-skin coat, and a German poacher admitted to getting $50,000 a year from illegal skins. Here, then, is another serious risk brought about by man's — or woman's — caprice. So we must now put the leopard with the tiger in *Category B*.

The *Jaguar,* the fourth of the roaring cats, seems relatively safe for the time being in the jungles of Central and South America and can be put with fair confidence in *Category B*.

The *Snow Leopard,* or *Ounce,* the smallest and least-known of the roarers, inhabits a terrain so inhospitable that it is not likely to attract the developer in the foreseeable future. Nevertheless, in these days one never knows what new discovery may transform the bleak mountains into hives of industry. Or perhaps its lovely skin might suddenly become fashionable too. So let the snow leopard be in *Category B*.

The *Cheetah.* All reports suggest a very precarious position for this unique animal, already almost extinct in Asia. We cannot attribute the cause of its recent decline immediately to man, though I have little doubt his shadow is in the background. To what extent the catching and export of wild cheetahs to India goes on, I do not know; in the present parlous state of the animal it ought to be stopped. In 1960 there were only fifty-eight in the whole Kruger National Park in South Africa; in 1961 Major Ian Grimwood considered they were threatened with extinction in Kenya; in 1963 there were reported to be about two hundred left in Iran but the "protected" area in which they live is now vulnerable to motor vehicles. So without hesitation I put the cheetah in my *Category D* for danger.

The *Puma,* because it lives partly in the continent of North America where large areas have been set aside under a planned conservation program and partly in the still undeveloped regions of South America, seems the best placed of all the big cats and even able to use the reserves as a springboard for a comeback into more settled districts. I think I shall be optimistic and put it in my highest group for safety: *Category A.*

The *Caracal* has become so scarce in Asia that we cannot be too happy about it in Africa; so with some misgivings I put it at present in *Category B.*

I have one more category to define. I call it *Q,* standing for a big question mark. We know so little of so many species — a third of the whole family — that we cannot hazard a forecast about their future at all. Enumeration is the first step toward conservation. E. P. Gee tells me, for example, that he does not know anyone who has seen the rusty-spotted cat of southern India in recent years. Is it now extinct, or has no one been interested in looking for it? It still occurs in Ceylon and is apparently fairly common in one area of southwestern India. In contrast, the evidence from Malaya and Borneo (see p. 73) suggests that the flat-headed cat really is very rare. According to Dr. Paul Leyhausen, the position of the golden cat in West Africa is extremely precarious; so is that of the ocelot, margay, and their relatives in America, because of their popularity both as pets and for furs. So, while admitting that our basis of knowledge is shaky in many cases, I would place the remaining cats thus:

Category A

Old World: Serval, African wildcat, European wildcat, jungle cat, leopard cat. New World: bobcat, jaguarundi.

Category B

Lynx (all races except Spanish), fishing cat, little spotted cat.

Category C

Black-footed cat, clouded leopard, Spanish lynx.

Category D

African golden cat, flat-headed cat, margay, ocelot.

Category Q

Old World: Bornean red cat, Chinese desert cat, marbled cat, Pallas's cat,

rusty-spotted cat, sand cat, Temminck's cat. New World: Andean cat, Geoffroy's cat, kodkod, pampas cat.

On this listing we have eight kinds in the comparative safety of A; eight
in B requiring a watching brief; three species and a race safe only in C
under the wing of conservation; probably five kinds in immediate danger;
and the remaining eleven are wrapped in present mystery. I do not think
any of this calls for complacence.

Against the thirty-five wild cats, I am afraid we have to put the feral
house cat as a debit, an ally or camp follower of man the destroyer. Whenever men camp or colonize, sooner or later they bring cats, first to keep
them company, then to hunt the rats and mice they have inadvertently introduced to successive devastated Edens. The cats escape and multiply and
turn their attention to the indigenous fauna. Their effect is particularly
heavy on islands with colonies of seabirds nesting in the open. On Ascen-
sion Island they have driven all but one species of tern to nest on offshore
stacks; from Christmas Island, amid the secrecy of the British atomic tests,
came a *cri du coeur* from a bird-loving sergeant which the International
Council for Bird Preservation did its best to answer. Australasia, the catless
continent, is catless no more. I was appalled at the number of feral cats —
tabby, ginger, pure white, but all as wild as the wildest of wild cats — which
we saw in North Queensland and in Cape York. Islands with endemic
flightless species have suffered disastrously from pets turned predator. No
doubt there are now cats in Antarctica. Only the mongoose, when introduced into the West Indies, has wrought more havoc, because it kills snakes,
which most cats avoid.

The future for the Felidae, as for all wild animals, is in our hands. These
great animals and their lesser brethren, so marvelously and diversely
adapted, have thrilled me since I was a boy pressing my nose as close as I
dared to the bars of their cages in the Antwerp Zoo. If what I have set down
in these pages has impressed you at all with the excitement, interest, and
indeed the affection these fine beasts of prey inspire, then I hope you will
give your support to those who nationally and internationally are working
to save them and the rest of the world's infinite variety of creatures.

Appendix I:
Checklist of the Family Felidae

IN COMPILING this list I have consulted the following authorities: *Checklist of Palaearctic and Indian Mammals 1758 to 1946* by J. R. Ellerman and T. C. S. Morrison-Scott, published by the Trustees of the British Museum in 1951; *Southern African Mammals 1758 to 1951: A Reclassification* by the same authors and R. W. Hayman, published in 1953; *A Checklist of African Mammals* by G. M. Allen (Bulletin of the Museum of Comparative Zoology No. 83), published by Harvard University in 1939; *A Handlist of Malaysian Mammals* by F. N. Chasen (Bulletin of the Raffles Museum No. 15), published in 1940; *The Mammals of North America* by E. Raymond Hall and Keith R. Kelson, published by Ronald Press in 1959; *Catalogo de los Mammiferos de America del Sur* by Angel Cabrera, published by the Argentine Museum of Natural Sciences, 1957 to 1961; and *Das Fellmuster der wildlebenden Katzenarten* by Ingrid Weigel, published as a supplement to Volume 9 of *Säugetierkundliche Mitteilungen* in 1961.

The first scientific name given is that of the genus, of which I am only recognizing three; the second is the name of the species; names in parentheses are those of the subgenera into which Ellerman and Morrison-Scott and other authors have split the genus *Felis*. I have given some alternative English names; after them comes a brief summary of the animal's distribution and the conservation category as defined in Chapter 9.

Genus: FELIS

Felis silvestris
Schreber 1877, European Wildcat (Plates 4, 35). Seven races, including the Scottish *grampia*, from Spain to the Caucasus and Asia Minor; not in Scandinavia. A.

Felis libyca
Forster 1780, African Wildcat, Indian Desert Cat (Plate 11). Twelve races from Mediterranean islands (Majorca, Corsica, Sardinia, Crete) and North Africa to Turkestan and India. A.

Note: Weigel combines these two in one species with between twenty and thirty races.

Felis margarita
Loche 1858, Sand Cat (Plate 11). Three races in deserts of North Africa, Arabia,

and Russian Turkestan (Turkmenia). Q.

Felis bieti

Milne-Edwards 1892, Chinese Desert Cat (Plate 23). Three races in deserts and steppes of Mongolia, Kansu, and Szechwan. Q.

Felis nigripes

Burchell 1822, Black-footed Cat (Plate 11). Karroo and Kalahari Deserts. C.

Felis chaus

Guldenstadt 1776, Jungle Cat (Plate 22). Nine races in Egypt, Asia Minor east to India, west China, Ceylon, and Southeast Asia. A.

Felis catus

Linnaeus 1758, House Cat (Plate 36). Worldwide, introduced by man.

Felis (Otocolobus) manul

Pallas 1776, Pallas's Cat (Plate 23). Three races in mountains and steppes of Asian U.S.S.R., Afghanistan, Baluchistan, Kashmir, Tibet, and western China. A.

Felis (Lynx) lynx

Linnaeus 1758, Canada or Northern Lynx (Plates 33, 34). Six races, including *pardina* in Spain, from Europe across Asia, including Asia Minor, to Sakhalin; and in North America to northern U.S. B; Spanish race C.

Felis (Lynx) rufa

Schreber 1777, Bobcat, Red Lynx (Plates 31, 32). Eleven races from Canada to Panama. A.

Felis (Caracal) caracal

Schreber 1776, Caracal, African Lynx (Plates 2, 8, 9). Four races throughout Africa, except the rain forests, Arabia northeast to Turkestan, Afghanistan and northwestern India. B.

Felis (Leptailurus) serval

Schreber 1776, Serval (Plates 2, 10, 11). Two races throughout Africa. A.

Felis (Pardofelis) marmorata

Martin 1837, Marbled Cat (Plate 20). Two races from northeastern India, Nepal, Burma, to Southeast Asia, Sumatra, and Borneo. Q.

Felis (Profelis) aurata

Temminck 1827, African Golden Cat (Plate 11). Tropical Africa. D.

Felis (Profelis) temmincki

Vigors and Horsfield 1827, Temminck's Cat, Golden Cat (Plate 21). Three races in southern China, Tibet, northeastern India, Malaya, and Sumatra. Q.

Felis (Prionailurus) bengalensis

Kerr 1792, Leopard Cat (Plate 25). Six races from southern China and India throughout Southeast Asia and its islands to the Philippines. A.

Felis (Prionailurus) rubiginosa

Geoffrey 1831, Rusty-spotted Cat (Plate 24). Two races in India and Ceylon. Q.

Felis (Prionailurus) viverrina

Bennett 1833, Fishing Cat (Plate 24). Parts of India, Ceylon, Malay Peninsula, Java, and Sumatra. B.

Felis (Prionailurus) planiceps
Vigors and Horsfield 1827, Flat-headed Cat (Plate 23). Malay Peninsula, Sumatra, Malacca, and Borneo. D.

Felis (Badiofelis) badia
Gray 1874, Bornean Red Cat (Plate 23). Borneo. Q.

Felis (Oncifelis) geoffroyi
D'Orbigny and Gervais 1843, Geoffroy's Cat (Plate 29). Five races from Bolivian Andes through Paraguay, Uruguay, and Argentina to Patagonia. Q.

Felis (Oncifelis) tigrina
Schreber 1775, Little Spotted Cat (Plate 28). Four races in Central and South America from Costa Rica to Peru and southeastern Brazil. *Note:* Weigel calls this species *pardinoides* and applies *tigrina* to the margay (see below). B.

Felis (Oncifelis) guigna
Molina 1810, Kodkod (Plate 29). Two races in Chile. Q.

Felis (Leopardus) wiedi
Schinz 1821, Margay (Plate 28). Eleven races from Mexico to southeastern Brazil. D.

Felis (Leopardus) pardalis
Linnaeus 1758, Ocelot (Plate 27). Eleven races from extreme southern U.S. to Bolivia and northern Argentina. D.

Felis (Lynchailurus) colocolo
Molina 1810, Pampas Cat (Plate 29).

Seven races in Brazil, Bolivia, Ecuador, Peru, Chile, and Argentina. *Note:* Weigel calls this species *pajeros*. Q.

Felis (Oreailurus) jacobita
Cornalia 1856, Andean Cat (Plate 29). Mountains of Peru, Bolivia, Chile, and Argentina. Q.

Felis (Puma) concolor
Linnaeus 1771, Puma, or Mountain Lion or Cougar (Frontispiece, Plate 26). Twenty-nine races from western Canada to Patagonia. A.

Felis (Herpailurus) yagouarundi
Geoffroy 1803, Jaguarundi (Plate 30). Nine races from southeastern U.S. to northern Argentina. A.

Felis (Neofelis) nebulosa
Griffith 1821, Clouded Leopard (Plate 20). Three races in northern India, southern China, Burma, Malay Peninsula, Southeast Asia, Formosa, Sumatra, and Borneo. C.

Genus: PANTHERA

Panthera (Uncia) uncia
Schreber 1775, Snow Leopard, Ounce (Plates 18, 19). Mountains of central Asia. B.

Panthera leo
Linnaeus 1758, Lion (Plates 2, 5, 15, 16). Two races, in tropical and South Africa; and in India (Gir Forest only). C.

Panthera tigris
Linnaeus 1758, Tiger (Plates 3, 12, 13, 14). Six races in Siberia, China, India, Persia, Burma, Malay Peninsula, Java, Sumatra, Bali (?). B.

Panthera onca
Linnaeus 1758, Jaguar (Plates 3, 27). Eight races from extreme southeastern U.S. to latitude 40° south. B.

Panthera pardus
Linnaeus 1758, Leopard Panther (Plates 7, 17). Fourteen races from southeastern Russia and Asia Minor throughout Asia to Ceylon and Java; and throughout Africa. B.

Genus: ACINONYX

Acinonyx jubatus
Schreber 1776, Cheetah, Hunting Leopard (Plates 1, 2, 8). Two races, in Africa and Iran, apparently extinct elsewhere in Asia. D.

Appendix II: Principal Sources

IN THE WRITING of this book several hundred books and articles in scientific journals have been consulted, so to present a short list for those who would like to read more about the cats of the world has not been easy. Except for Cahalane's book, I have not included titles covering the mammals of a continent and I have confined myself to a few classics and to books easily accessible to British and American readers either in shops or libraries. So, with apologies to many authors living and dead, here is my short selection.

George A. Best, F. Edmond-Blanc, and R. C. Whiting
    Records of Big Game. 11th edition (Africa). London: Rowland Ward, 1962.

Reginald G. Burton
    The Book of the Tiger. London: Hutchinson, 1933.

Victor H. Cahalane
  Mammals of North America. New
  York: Macmillan, 1947.

Harry R. Caldwell
  Blue Tiger. New York: Abingdon
  Press, 1924.

Frederick W. Champion
  With a Camera in Tiger-Land. Lon-
  don: Chatto & Windus, 1927.
  The Jungle in Sunlight and Shadow.
  London: Chatto & Windus, 1933.

Jim Corbett
  *The Man-eating Leopard of Rudra-
  prayag.* London and New York:
  Oxford, 1948.

C. A. W. Guggisberg
  Simba: The Life of the Lion. Phila-
  delphia: Chilton Books, 1963.

Theodor Haltenorth
  Die Wildkatze. Wittenberg-Luther-
  stadt, 1957. Neue Brehme-Büche-
  rei 189.

St. George Mivart
  The Cat. London: Murray, 1881.

John H. Patterson
  The Man-Eaters of Tsavo. London:
  Macmillan, 1907.

Sir Alfred Pease
  The Book of the Lion. New York:
  Scribner, 1914.

Reginald I. Pocock
  Catalogue of the Genus Felis. Lon-
  don: British Museum (Natural
  History), 1951.

Grace Pond
  The Observer's Book of Cats. London: Warne, 1959.

Theodore Roosevelt and Edmund
Heller
  *Life-Histories of African Game Ani-
  mals.* 2 vols. New York: Scribner,
  1914.

James Stevenson-Hamilton
  Wild Life in South Africa. London:
  Cassell, 1947.

Bruce S. Wright
  The Ghost of North America. New
  York: Vantage Press, 1959.

Stanley P. Young and Edward A.
Goldman
  *The Puma: Mysterious American
  Cat.* Washington, D.C.: American
  Wildlife Institute, 1946.

The World Wildlife Fund

THE WORLD WILDLIFE FUND is an international charitable foundation for raising money to save the world's wildlife and wild places. It is devoted to the concept that conservation is for the benefit of man, who has ethical, esthetic, and economic responsibilities to preserve at least part of the natural environment in which he has evolved. At one end of its scale of activities it is trying to save certain animal and plant species from imminent extinction — a kind of modern Noah's Ark; at the other it extends over the whole intricate relationship betwen water, soil, plants, animals, and man himself. It is concerned with the right use of land — in short, with the *ecology of man.*

Man must learn to apply the science of ecology to himself. He must also recognize that he has responsibilities in this context, responsibilities of trusteeship for the natural world over which he now exercises so much control. Take, for example, oil pollution and freshwater pollution, and toxic chemical sprays; and take the extermination of animal and plant species — an utterly irrevocable process . . .

At this moment more than a thousand kinds of vertebrate animals are threatened with imminent extinction at the hands of man. Species that have taken hundreds of thousands of years to evolve their unique adaptations to their environment are being wiped out in a few decades because they do not seem to have a "use," or because not enough people care one way or the other.

The World Wildlife Fund was set up under Swiss federal law on September 28, 1961, with an announcement that the wildlife situation in the world at large amounted to "a state of emergency for animals" and with the publication of a World Wildlife Charter for submission to the United Nations.

The British National Appeal of the World Wildlife Fund (which is established as a charity for tax purposes) has Prince Philip as its President.

To fulfill its aims and ambitions, the World Wildlife Fund urgently requires money. Any contributions or inquiries should be addressed to:

Executive Secretary
The World Wildlife Fund
1816 Jefferson Place, N.W.
Washington, D.C. 20036

The address of the headquarters in Switzerland is:

The Secretary-General
World Wildlife Fund (International)
Morges, Vaud, Switzerland

Index